BLUE BOOK

GOLD EDITION

BY MARK KLIMEK

NCLEX®, NCLEX-RN® are registered trademarks of the National Council of State Boards of Nursing, Inc., which neither sponsors nor endorses this product.

ISBN – 978-1-962559-00-3

Published by kPub
Columbus, Ohio

Chapter 7: Reduction of Risk Potential

Chapter 8: Physiological Adaptation

Intro from Mark
and how to use this book

I developed this resource with one goal in mind: to enable graduated nurses to refresh their knowledge base of the facts and principles essential for safe and effective nursing practice. By increasing their knowledge base, an exam candidate will greatly increase performance on the RN licensure examination. You cannot apply what you do not know. Over the decades I have found that a lack of fundamental facts is a major reason why candidates fail the licensure exam.

Most review books focus on multiple choice and "select all that apply" formats that require **application** of knowledge. I could not find a single resource that assisted students to refresh their **knowledge base**. The BEST way to learn facts is through **"drill"** where a student is asked a question then given the answer in a manner that can be repeated as often as necessary to master the content. This book is like using flash cards to learn facts. Simply cover up the answer when reading the question; then reveal to see if the answer is correct.

Special Note:
With the arrival of **the NCLEX-RN® NextGen format**, this resource has become more useful than ever. The majority of the questions asked in this book require you to "fill in the blank" or to complete a table. Filling in the blank is a new format called **CLOZE**. Therefore, this resource prepares you for cloze questions. The tabular questions prepare you for the **multiple response table format** questions. Another benefit of this book for NextGen is that many of the questions are "Yes" or "No". These give you direction as to what you should select in **"Select all that apply."**

If I were your personal tutor as you prepare to take the NCLEX-RN® Licensure Exam...

> I would sit down with you and tell you everything I want you to know before you take the exam... and it would be exactly what is in this Blue Book. (As well as what we cover in the Klimek Review lectures.)

> I would ask you thousands of questions... and they would be exactly the questions I have written for you in this Blue Book.

> I would give you the BEST ANSWER to every question I ask... and those answers are in this Blue Book. The question is on the left side of the page; the answer is on the right. Cover the answer while you ask yourself the question, so that you are truly building and testing your knowledge. Don't waste time re-reading questions that you know. You may want to highlight the questions you don't need to read again.

> After you are confident of all of these questions and answers, you practice applying this knowledge in other multiple-choice test questions.

If you have a friend or family member who wants to help you study, you could have them quiz you from this Blue Book.

I would encourage you to <u>hope</u> that the computer gives you the maximum number of questions on your NCLEX® exam, so that more of these questions have an opportunity to appear on your test!

I would require that you <u>master</u> this information before you take the exam, to give you both knowledge and <u>confidence</u>. (Should you expect to be 100% confident when you are taking your exam? NO! The computer will keep asking you questions until it can identify what you don't know, and at that point <u>no</u> one feels confident!)

Three frequently asked questions (FAQ's):
- Can I teach you everything you should have learned in your nursing program? **No.**
- Can I help you focus your mind on the most important things you need to know right now? **Yes.**
- Can you pass the NCLEX-RN® exam? **Absolutely.**

If the Blue Book has proven to be beneficial to you and you're eager for more comprehensive guidance, I developed courses in conjunction with this book over the past three decades. Klimek Reviews offers online on-demand courses, in-person full reviews, and online tutoring formats. Discover the invaluable insights and expertise that have empowered countless individuals on their journey to success. Explore further at:

- **On-Demand Courses**: https://klimekreviews.com/courses/
- **In-Person Reviews**: https://klimekreviews.com/register/

CHAPTER 1

Management Of Care

ADVANCE DIRECTIVES

Name five advance directives.	Power of attorney, living will, POLST/MOLST, Do not resuscitate orders, Organ donation card
A living will is a legal document that tells HCP's how you want to be _____ if you cannot make your own decisions in an _____.	Treated, Emergency.
A durable power of attorney for health care is a legal document that specifies a _____ of your _____ who is authorized to make health care decisions for you if you are _____.	Person. Choice, Unable.
A 'do not resuscitate' order informs care givers you do not want certain specified _____ _____ measures if your _____ or _____ stop.	Life-support, Heart, Breathing
POLST/MOLST provide _____ to HCP's about life sustaining treatment when you have a _____ condition or are at _____of life.	Guidance, Terminal, End.
What is DNI?	Do not intubate.
Can a floor nurse obtain agreement of the client to be a organ donor?	NO, only organ donation personnel obtain patient consent to be a organ donor.
An organ donor is said to be deceased when the _____ is dead but the patient's _____ is still _____ and their _____ are still _____.	Brain, Heart, beating Lungs, breathing.
A patient with terminal cancer executes a legal document saying they do not want a tube feeding if their condition deteriorates and they cannot eat orally. The above is an example of a _____.	POLST Note: POLST/MOLST are executed when the patient is terminal or at end of life.

A healthy 55-year-old male executes a document expressing his wish not to receive tube feedings if he is unable to voice his wishes and is unable to eat orally. He executed what document?	A living will. Note: most living wills are executed when the client is still relatively healthy and not terminal or dying.
A patient going for emergency brain surgery signs a form stating he does not want CPR performed if his heart stops. This is an example of a _____.	DNR
All advance directives must be written and approved by a professional lawyer,	NO, anyone can write their own if there is some notation that it was indeed the person who signed it.
All advance directives cannot be changed once written and signed. True or false.	False, advance directives can be changed at any time by the client.
Which advance directives need to be posted at the bedside?	POLST/MOLST
Which advance directives must be in the medical record?	All of them.

CLIENT RIGHTS

A patient can expect to be treated with _____regardless of race, gender, color, religion, age, marital status, sexual orientation, disability, or other state or condition.	Respect
Can a patient choose who they spend time with during hospitalization?	YES
Does every patient have the right to effective pain management?	YES
Does a patient have the right to treat healthcare personnel abusively verbally and /or physically?	No
Does the patient have a right to talk to or treat a roommate in any way they wish	No

Does a patient have right to break hospital safety protocols, such as no smoking etc.	No
Does a patient have the right to vote in ICU?	Yes
Does a patient have the right not to be restrained except when absolutely necessary for safety reasons?	Yes
Does a patient have the right to a clean environment?	Yes
Does a patient have the right to confidentiality?	Yes
Does a patient have the right to see their medical record?	Yes. There may be a legal delay in granting a request. A nurse is not authorized to grant permission to look at medical record instantly.
Can a patient choose their own physician or nurse.	Yes, the professional has privileges at the institution and has availability.
Can a patient refuse treatment?	Yes. If they refuse all treatment then they will sign out AMA, "Against medical advice."
Does a patient have the right to bring in their own food?	Yes
Does a patient have the right to dress in their own pajamas.	Yes

CONFIDENTIALITY AND PRIVACY

Can a nurse talk to the family of a patient without the patient's permission?	No
Can a nurse talk to a person who has power of attorney for health care without permission of the patient?	Yes, that is one of the purposes of the POA.
If a family member calls for information but the patient has not given permission for that person to know, What should the nurse say?	"I can neither confirm nor deny whether that person is here or not here."

Can a minor have protection from parental/guardian knowledge under confidentiality laws?	No, not unless they are an emancipated minor or a female who is or suspects she is pregnant.
If an HCP wants to see the medical record of a patient who is not their patient and there is no referral ordered... what should the nurse say?	"No, you cannot see the medical record without a referral."
If a hospital administrator wants to see the medical record of a patient the nurse should say?	"No, unless you can document why you have a legitimate need to know."
What is physical privacy?	Separation of the patient by space or barriers.
What is psychological privacy?	The perception by the client that they have privacy.
What is the most common way nurses violate a patient's psychological privacy?	Talking about other patients, themselves, or other staff members.
If a nurse wants to talk to a patient about their health situation but it is a semiprivate room, what should the nurse do?	Ask the other patient to leave the room or remove the patient from the room and talk privately...the same goes for visitors.

DELEGATION

Does a RN delegate to another RN?	No, a RN ASSIGNS another RN.
To whom does a RN delegate?	To a LPV/LVN and UAP. Remember you **D**elegate **D**own and **A**ssign **A**cross
Does a RN delegate to a physical therapist, respiratory therapist, or social worker?	No, Rn's refer to or collaborate with these other professionals.
Can the RN delegate starting an IV to a LPN?	No
Can a RN delegate administering a blood transfusion to a LPN?	No
Can a RN delegate patient teaching to a LPN?	NO. But the LPN can reinforce or review teaching the RN has already performed.

Can a RN delegate hanging or mixing IV medications to a LPN?	No
Can a RN delegate assessing a changing situation to a LPN?	No
Can a RN delegate evaluating a patient to the LPN?	No
Can a RN delegate planning care to a LPN?	No
Can a RN delegate an admission assessment, transfer within hospital assessment, or discharge assessment to a LPN?	No
Can a RN delegate an IV push medication administration to a LPN?	No
What CAN the RN delegate to a LPN?	Direct patient care, assessment of, and non-IV medication administration to STABLE clients.
What four things can a RN not delegate to an UAP?	Charting about the patient (they can document what they did), medication administration (except for topical skin lotions), assessments (except VS on stable patients), and treatments (except non-sterile at home.
Which of these could not be delegated to an UAP performing patient care on a stable patient in their home? Trach suctioning, wound dressing change, administering a tube feeding, straight catheterization of the bladder, changing a central line dressing.	Changing a central line dressing is RN only. The other four are NON-STERILE in the home therefore can be performed by an UAP.

ETHICS

What principle claims people are free from control by others?	Autonomy
What principle states it is right to take positive action to help others?	Beneficence

What principle says it is right to do NO harm?	Non-maleficence
What principle states actions should be fair?	Justice
What principle claims it is right to keep promises?	Fidelity
When a nurse includes a patient in the decision-making process what ethical principle makes it right?	Autonomy
When a nurse takes the position that children should not be immunized because there could be many unknown effects, the principle being used is _____.	Non-maleficence
When a nurse takes the position that children should be immunized because it has benefits, the principle being used is _____.	Beneficence
When a nurse tells a patient that they will be back in 30 minutes and interrupts a conversation with another nurse to go back to the patient in 30 minutes, what principle is in effect?	Fidelity
What principle states that the greatest good comes from telling the truth?	Veracity
Does confidentiality mean you never discuss patient information with anyone?	No, it means you only discuss with others that NEED to know.
What are examples of information you cannot keep confidential?	Sexually transmitted disease, abuse, threat to kill/harm self or others.

MANAGING STAFF CONFLICT

What are the six conflict management strategies in nursing?	Accommodating, Avoiding, Collaborating, Competing, Compromising, Forcing.
Which of these strategies is most used by nurses to resolve conflict?	Compromising

Which 3 styles of conflict resolution are least effective?	Competing, Avoiding, Forcing.
What style should be used when the leader highly values their goal, the decision is going to be unpopular no matter what, it must be made immediately, and it is at crisis level?	Competing, because it is most directive and autocratic.
What style might be effective when the leader really does not have a strong sense of what needs to be done, the issue is minor and there is no sense of urgency	Accommodating, because the resolution solution is not going to have any appreciable negative consequences.
What style might be effective if more time is needed to formulate thought or response, time constraints demand a delay, or risk of confrontation is not worth gains.	Avoiding
What style might be effective if both parties have strong belief in their positions but value the relationship highly. There is time to make the decision/resolution, i.e not a crisis.	Compromising
What style might be effective if no one is sure what to do to resolve the conflict but value peace in the atmosphere?	Collaborating, because this involves a lot of brainstorming.

NURSE AND THE LAW I

Assault (define)	A threat or an attempt to make bodily contact with another person without that person's consent.
Battery (define)	An assault that is carried out.
Common law (define)	Law resulting from a court decision that is then followed when other cases involving similar circumstances arise.

Malpractice	An act of negligence--commonly used when speaking of negligent acts committed by a person working in a certain profession, such as medicine or nursing.
Ethics	A system that defines actions with respect to their being judged right or wrong.
False imprisonment	Unjustifiable restraint or prevention of the movement of a person without proper consent.
Misdemeanor	A wrong of less seriousness than a felony.
Good Samaritan law	Law that gives certain persons legal protection when giving aid to someone in an emergency.
Felony	A wrong of serious nature.
Negligence	Performing an act that a reasonable and comparable person under similar circumstances would not do, or failing to perform an act that a reasonable and comparable person under similar circumstances would do.
Invasion of privacy	A wrongful act that violates the right of a person to be let alone.
Liable	Being accountable, responsible, or answerable for an act.
Libel	A written untruthful statement about a person that subjects him/her to ridicule or contempt.
Slander	A spoken untruthful statement about a person that subjects him/her to ridicule or contempt.

NURSE AND THE LAW II

How could a nurse be convicted of assault?	If the client perceives that the nurse intends to do a procedure without consent or justification.

How could a nurse be convicted of battery?	If the nurse willfully touched a client in any manner that is wrong in some way.
Clients have a right to refuse nursing interventions (T/F)	TRUE
If a nurse uses restraints to keep a client, who is a danger to himself, in bed, the nurse is likely to be convicted of false imprisonment. (T/F)	False, you can detain/restrain a person against their will if they are: 1) a threat to self; 2) a threat to others.
In order to legally sign as a witness to informed consent, the nurse must have been present when the physician and client discussed the procedure. (T/F)	False. You are only witnessing that the patient was the one who signed the consent.
It is NOT necessary for the nurse to determine if the client understands what the physician said in order to witness an informed consent. (T/F)	True. You are only witnessing a signature.
Can a patient legally sign an informed consent after they have received the premedication analgesic for a procedure?	No. The patient would be considered to be under the influence of a mind-altering drug. The consent would be invalid.
Name three groups of people who cannot give legal consent.	Minor, unconscious client (even under influence of CNS drugs), mentally ill
In an emergency situation, when client and family cannot give consent, consent is assumed and treatment proceeds. (T/F)	TRUE
The legality of no code or slow code orders is well-established in the courts. (T/F)	False, no definitive policy in the courts exists at this time--dealt with on a case-by-case basis.

PREFICES

ante-	Before in time or place (ie: "antepartal"-- before giving birth)
im-; in-	"Not" or "into"

intra-	Occurring within
inter-	Between
per-	Throughout, completely, a large amount
ec-	Out of
e-; ex-	Out from, away from, outside
iso-	A combining form meaning 'equal'
para-	Similar, beside

PRIORITIZATION PROTOCOLS

How many different prioritization protocols are there?	Four
What are the four most common prioritization protocols used by nurses.	Stable vs Unstable, ABC, CAB, Maslow hierarchies
Stable vs Instable is used to prioritize when the nurse is dealing with...	**More** than one patient simultaneously.
ABC stands for...	Airway, breathing, circulation.
ABC is used to prioritize when there is _____ _____ _____ and all the needs/problems are _____.	**ONLY ONE** patient, **Physiological.**
CAB stands for...	Circulation, airway, breathing.
CAB is used to prioritize when there is only _____ _____ and their problem is of a _____ nature.	**ONE** patient, **CARDIAC**

What is the order of priority when using Maslow in nursing care?	Physiological Safety (Unless at an accident scene then safety is first) Comfort, Psychological needs, Social needs, Spiritual needs.
Maslow's hierarchy is used when the nurse is caring for _____ _____ _____ and the needs are _____ NOT just _____.	**ONLY ONE** patient, Multidimensional, Physiological.
In a NextGen case study which of the four prioritization protocols is never used?	Since a case study is always only about ONE patient the **stable vs unstable is NOT** used in a case study.
Does the NextGen licensure exam include questions where you will use stable vs unstable?	YES, quite a few, but they will always be "stand alone questions" and involve MORE than ONE patient simultaneously.

SUFFIXES

-pathy	Disease, suffering
-penia	Lack, deficiency of
-sect	To cut
-plast	Plastic surgery on a specified part
-sclerosis	Hardening of a tissue by inflammation, deposition of mineral salts; an infiltration of connective tissue fibers
-centesis	A perforation or puncture
-genic	Produce, originate, become
-emia	Blood
-otomy	Cutting
-pexy	Fixation of something

-atresia	Condition of occlusion
-desis	Binding, fusing
-cele	Combining form meaning a tumor or swelling or a cavity
-cis	Cut, kill
-rhapy; -rrhapy	Joining in a seam, suturation
-scope; -scopy	Instrument for observation
-osis	Indicates condition, process
-oma	Tumor
-ostomy	Surgical opening
-stasis	Stoppage
-itis	Inflammation
-ology	Study of ; knowledge, science
-lysis	Breaking down
-ectomy	Surgical removal of
-tripsy	Crushing of something by a surgical instrument
-ase	Used in naming enzymes
-gram; -graphy	Write; record

TEACHING-LEARNING PRINCIPLES

When teaching a patient, the nurse assesses what FIRST?	The patient's readiness to learn.
What 3 things are involved in the patient's readiness to learn?	1) Physical readiness 2) Emotional readiness 3) Intellectual readiness

What are some examples of physical readiness.	If they are comfortable, they are more likely ready. Is the environment physically conducive to learning (think noise and privacy)? Also are they blind or deaf? as these could challenge learning in unique ways.
What are some examples of emotional readiness to learn.	Anxiety, fear, guilt, grief, denial, psychological symptoms all interfere with learning. Do they WANT to learn...BIG ONE!
What is meant by intellectual readiness?	Is the patient cognitively to understand the methods used to teach.
Should you ever ask if they are ready to learn?	Absolutely!
Another principle of teaching learning is assessing their best LEARNING STYLE. What are the three learning styles?	Auditory, Visual, Kinesthetic(psychomotor).
Should you approach teaching at an average level of intelligence and vocabulary?	No, approach the patient from their own unique level. Assess this through conversation.
Should the client play an active role in the teaching process?	Absolutely, get them active.
Should you ever ask a patient to repeat their understanding of what you just said?	Yes. It clarifies and documents understanding.
What is the BEST way to evaluate if teaching has been successful?	The patient demonstrates a **change**. The change can be in behavior, or condition. Remember, just because they can repeat back what you said does not mean they learned.
A patient says, "I don't want to learn this, I don't need to" What is your assessment?	They are most likely in denial and teaching at this time will be unsuccessful.

CHAPTER 2

SAFETY & INFECTION CONTROL

ACCIDENTAL POISONING

Should vomiting be induced after ingestion of cleaning product?	No (when the product comes back up, it will damage the esophagus again)
At what age are accidental poisonings most common?	2 years old
If a child swallows a potentially poisonous substance, what should be done first?	Call medical help
Should vomiting be induced after ingestion of gasoline?	No – not for gas or any other petroleum products
When taking a child to the ER after accidental poisoning has occurred what must accompany the child to the ER?	The suspected poison
An elderly client is a (high/low) risk for accidental poisoning?	High – due to poor eyesight
What types of chemicals cause burns to oral mucosa when ingested?	Lye, caustic cleaners
Children at highest risk for seizure activity after ingestion are those who have swallowed _____ and _____.	Drugs and insecticides
Can impaired skin integrity ever be an appropriate nursing diagnosis when poisoning has occurred?	Yes, when lye or caustic agents have been ingested.
School age children are (high/low) risk for accidental poisoning.	High

ACQUIRED IMMUNE DEFICIENCY SYNDROME – AIDS

What virus causes AIDS?	HIV – human immunodeficiency virus
The AIDS virus invades helper _____ _____.	T-lymphocytes (CD4 cells)

AIDS is transmissible through what four routes?	Blood, sexual contact, breast feeding, across placenta in utero.
HIV is present in all body fluids (T/F)	True, but not transmitted by all – only blood, semen, and breast milk.
Name the five risk groups for AIDS	Homosexual/bisexual men, IV drug users, hemophiliacs, heterosexual partners of infected people, newborn children of infected women.
What is the first test for HIV antibodies?	HIV-1/2 Ag/Ab combination immuno assay (ELISA)
The rapid HIV test available in clinics and doctor's offices tests which body fluid?	Saliva
What tests confirm the ELISA?	Western Blot (IFA, PCR)
Which test is the best indicator of the progress of HIV disease?	The CD4 count
A CD4 count of under ___ is associated with the onset of AIDS-related symptoms.	500
A CD4 count of under ___ is associated with the onset of opportunistic infections.	200
Give 6 symptoms of HIV disease.	Anorexia, fatigue, weakness, night sweats, fever, diarrhea
Which two classes of drugs are given in combination for HIV sero-positivity?	NRTI's (nucleoside reverse transcriptase inhibitors) and PI's (protease inhibitors)
What do these drugs do?	They prevent viral replication
What does the physician hope to achieve with these drugs?	A delayed onset of AIDS for as long as possible (usually can delay onset for 10-15 years).
What is the most common NRTI used?	AZT (zidovudine)

What is the most challenging aspect of combination of drug therapy for HIV disease?	The number of pills that must be taken in 24 hours can be overwhelming. The frequency also makes it hard to remember – an alarm wristwatch is used.
Clients with AIDS (gain/lose) weight?	Lose
The typical pneumonia of AIDS is caused by _____ _____.	Pneumocystic carinii
What type of oral/esophageal infections do AIDS patients get?	Candida
What is the #1 cancer that AIDS patients get?	Kaposi's sarcoma
Kaposi's sarcoma is a cancer of the ____.	Skin
Can AIDS patients get lymphomas?	Yes
What lab findings are present in AIDS?	Decreased RBC, WBC, platelets
If the AIDS patient has leukopenia they will be on _____ _____.	Protective (reverse) isolation
Without leukopenia the AIDS patient will be on _____ precautions.	Standard precautions or blood and body fluid precautions
When the AIDS patient has a low platelet count, what is indicated?	Bleeding precautions: No IM's, no rectal temperatures, other bleeding precautions.
Does AIDS require a single room?	Yes – if WBC counts are low
When do you need a gown with AIDS?	If you are going to be contaminated with secretions.
When do you need a mask with AIDS?	Not usually unless they have an infection caused by an airborne microorganism.

When do you need goggles with AIDS?	Suctioning, central line start, arterial procedures
If an AIDS patient's blood contaminates a countertop, with what do you clean?	1:10 solution of bleach and water
Are all articles used by AIDS patients double bagged?	No – only those contaminated with secretions.
Can AIDS patients leave the floor?	Yes, unless WBCs are very low.

ALLERGIES

Allergies are considered potential injury for the patient. (T/F)	True. Therefore, they are high priority because they are a SAFETY need.
What drug is given during emergency treatment of a severe allergic reaction?	Epinephrine IM by auto injector.
Where is an autoinjection of epinephrine given?	Outer mid-thigh.
Can you give an autoinjection through clothing?	Yes
Do you call 911or a rapid response team before you auto inject?	NO, auto inject first then call.
Can you give a second dose of epinephrine?	Yes, after 5 minutes if the patient does not improve.
What drug helps relieve the dyspnea of allergy?	Albuterol
Where should allergy alerts be placed when a client with allergies is hospitalized	Four places, Patient wears a wrist band, Noted in the heading of the medical record, Signage at the bedside, Medication administration pages.
What food allergies are associated with Latex allergy?	Avocado, kiwi, banana, passion fruit, plum, strawberry and tomato.

Can hospitals obtain latex free gloves?	Yes
Is tegaderm latex-free?	Yes
In what population of children is latex allergy most common.	Children with Spinal bifida where contract with latex early in life is frequent.

DEALING WITH THE VIOLENT CLIENT

The goal of nursing intervention in the care of the violent client is to prevent loss of _____ or to restore _____.	Control, control
Use of alcohol and/or drugs (decreases/increases) risk of violent behavior.	Increases
Pacing can be a warning sign of potential violence. (T/F)	True, as is any other form of increased motor activity.
If the client is not yet out of control, what is the #1 strategy to treat beginning violence?	Decrease environmental stimuli.
When a client is becoming violent you should move in close to them to provide a sense of security. (T/F)	False, allow them space or else they can get worse.
When approaching a violent client, the first thing you say is ...	My name is _____ and I am a nurse.
After identifying yourself, what do you say next?	Explain what you are going to do and ask if there are any questions.
When the client is having an overt violent outburst, you should NEVER be alone with them. (T/F)	TRUE
When you seek assistance to deal with the violent client, you should obtain _____ personnel.	Trained
Should you ever ask family or other patients to help you physically overcome a violent client?	NEVER

When a client is overtly and actively violent, they are given a chance to calm themselves down before being subdued. (T/F)	True, once enough trained personnel are present the client is told that if they don't control themselves, they will be controlled by us.
To promote efficient and safe accomplishment of physically controlling a violent client it is extremely important that…	Only one person talk during the procedure
When a client is losing control, it is very frightening to them if the nurse shows _____.	Fear
The best staff approach to control impulsive outbreaks of violence is…	Setting limits and doing it consistently.

EMERGENCY RESPONSE PROTOCOLS

In the case of a fire on the unit what is the order of a nurse's actions?	RACE **R**escue, **A**larm, **C**ontain, **E**xtinguish
What does rescue mean?	Remove a patient who is in the direct vicinity of the fire (in their room etc.)
How is rescue different than evacuation?	Rescue is removing a patient from the exact location of the fire. Evacuation is removal of patients from areas of potential fire SPREAD.
How does the RN contain or confine a fire?	By closing doors. And placing wet towels at the base of the door (prevent smoke spread).
When using a fire extinguisher what is the order of actions?	PASS **P**ull pin, **A**im at the base of fire, **S**queeze the trigger, **S**weep from side to side.
How should nurses evacuate patients from a building on fire?	Move patients across the unit to a stairwell then down. Remember across then down. DO NOT use an elevator.
If a nurse touches a stairwell door and it is hot what is the next action to take?	Do not open the door, move to another stairwell. If possible, place wet towels at the base of the door.

In the case of a natural disaster what are the two most important roles for the nurse?	Triage (prioritize) patients, Stabilize patients.
What are the four colors for the triage of patients at a mass casualty event?	Red, Yellow, Green, and Black. In that order of priority.
What color tag is given to a patient with life-threatening injuries who DO NOT have a chance for survival?	Black
What color tag is given to a patient with life-threatening injuries who HAS a chance of survival.	Red
What color tag is given to patients who can ambulate or self care to a limited extent.	Green
What color tag is given to a patient who is stable but needs immediate attention?	Yellow
What do area hospitals need to do when a natural disaster occurs?	Triage their patients and gather all stable clients for discharge (to make beds available).

IDENTIFYING A PATIENT

How many pieces of independent information are required for adequate identification of a patient in the health care setting?	A least two.
What are five acceptable unique patient identifiers?	Name, an assigned number, telephone number, date of birth, last four of social security.
Is a room number an acceptable identifier?	No
Is an armband an acceptable identifier?	No, it can be used to verify that the patient answers are accurate.
Does Joint Commission require armbands?	No
Does taping and armband to the bedside count as an acceptable identifier?	No

Can pictures be used as acceptable identifiers?	Yes, as long as this practice is institutional protocol.
Can a family member count as a acceptable identifier?	Only if they have power of attorney, (or parent/legal guardian)
Is an address an acceptable form of ID?	Yes
Is it safe practice to accept another nurses' verbal identification of a patient as identification?	No, just because another nurse identifies a patient does not mean they are correct
How often do you properly identify a patient?	Before every time you perform care. Yes, it does get redundant, but it is required.

LEAD POISONING

What lead level needs intervention?	50 to 60 micrograms/dl
With which class of drugs will a child with lead poisoning be treated?	Chelating agents
What do chelating agents do?	They increase the excretion of heavy metals.
The most frequent cause of lead poisoning is...	Ingestion of lead-based paint chips
Name three common chelating agents for lead poisoning.	EDTA, desferal, BAL in oil
List specific symptoms of lead poisoning.	Drowsiness, clumsiness, ataxia, seizures, coma, respiratory arrest.
Symptoms of lead poisoning show up in the _____ system.	Neurological

MEDICAL-SURGICAL ASEPSIS

In the chain of infection, hand washing breaks the mode of ____.	Transmission
The best way to decrease nosocomial infection is sterile technique. (T/F)	False, hand washing is the best way.

Sterile gloved hands must always be kept above the waist. (T/F)	TRUE
When putting on the second of a set of sterile gloves, you should grasp the cuff. (T/F)	False, reach under the cuff with the tip of the gloved fingers.
When putting on the first glove of a set of sterile gloves, you should grasp the cuff. (T/F?)	TRUE
When putting on the second glove of a set of sterile gloves, you must not use the thumb of the first hand. (T/F?)	TRUE
Airborne microorganisms travel on _____ or _____ particles.	Dust or water
Another name for medical asepsis is	Clean technique
Sensitivity (susceptibility) means...	The susceptibility of an organism to the bacterial action of a particular agent.
When unwrapping a sterile pack how should you unfold the top point?	Away from you.
Virulence means....	Ability of an organism to produce disease.
Another name for surgical asepsis is....	Sterile technique
What is the best location in a client's room to set up a sterile field?	On the over-bed table.
Medical aseptic techniques are aimed at reducing the number of organisms (T/F)	True, doesn't eliminate all, it just decreases the number.
What does bacteriostatic mean?	Having the capability to stop the growth of bacteria.
What does bacteriocidal mean?	Having the capability to kill bacteria.
What does nosocomial infection mean?	Infection acquired through contact with contamination in the hospital.

When pouring liquid onto a sterile field you should pour from a height of _____ to _____ inches above the field.	6 to 8
When you plan to use gloves for a procedure you do not need to wash hands before it. (T/F)	False, always wash even if you plan to use gloves.
Culture means....	Growing a colony of organisms, usually for the purpose of identifying them.
Surgical aseptic techniques render and keep articles free from all organisms. (T/F)	TRUE
You must never turn your back to a sterile field. (T/F)	TRUE
What must you do if you reach across a sterile field?	Consider the area contaminated and not use the articles in the area.
Micro-organisms grow best in a _____, _____, _____ place.	Warm, dark, moist
It is common practice to regard the edges of any sterile field as contaminated. (T/F)	True, the outer 1 inch is considered contaminated. You must not touch it with your sterile gloves.
Immediately after opening a bottle of sterile water, can you pour it directly into a sterile basin?	No, you must pour a few mL's out of the bottle into a waste container before you pour into the sterile basin. (This is called "lipping" the bottle.)

PATIENT ENVIRONMENT

Comfort range of relative humidity is...	30-60%
Which patients should be forbidden to smoke? Smoke alone?	Those with oxygen in the room, confused, sleepy, drugged clients
When applying restraints remember to...	Avoid bruising the skin, cutting off circulation, accidental entangling
List ways to ensure privacy...	Use drapes and screens during care in semi-private rooms.
Plastic pillowcases are _____. (disadvantages)	Hot and slippery

When using restraints with clients who object, don't forget about _____ _____.	False imprisonment
Individuals who are ill are _____ sensitive to noise than individuals who are well.	More
When you are not at the bedside the bed should always be...	In the lowest position
Can nurses be held liable for an accident resulting from a client not being told how to use the call light?	Yes
Dangers associated with drafts are...	Circulation of micro-organisms on air currents.
The first thing a nurse should do when a client objects to side rails is...	Explain why they are being used
The comfort range of temperature is...	68° to 74°
Is having the client verbally identify himself considered adequate for safety?	No. Also, confirming identification bands with what the patient says is acceptable.
Bed side rails should be up for the following individuals....	Elderly clients, unconscious, babies, young children, restless, confused.
The symptoms of sensory overload and sensory deprivation are...	Fear, panic, depression, inability to concentrate, restlessness, agitation
If a family member asks to have the side rails down while they are in the room, you should...	Remember that you are responsible for the client's safety--not his family, it is unsafe to permit this.
Pillows are sterilized between uses. (T/F?)	FALSE

RESTRAINTS

Are restraints in hospitals used as a first course of action or a last resort?	As a LAST resort.
What are some types of physical restraint?	Holding a patient down, mitts, elbow restraints, vests, belts, jackets, wrist and ankle restraints.

What is an example of chemical restraint?	Use of sedative medications
Can restraints be used to keep a patient from harming self?	Yes
Can restraints be used to prevent a patient from harming others?	Yes
Can restraints be used to keep a patient from falling.	Yes, but only if on elevated surfaces. Keeping the bed low or a mattress on the floor is preferable to restraint.
Can restraints be used to keep a patient from removing lines needed in their care?	Yes
When does the nurse need to notify the HCP that restraints are being used?	Immediately
Are HCP orders required for ALL restraint use?	YES!
How often do patients in restraint need to be checked?	Every 15 minutes
How often do restraints need to be released momentarily or rotated?	Every 2 hours
How long should adults be kept in restraints without additional medical evaluation?	4 hours
How long should older children and adolescents be in restraints without additional evaluation.	2 hours
How long should be children under 9 be in restraints without additional medical evaluation?	1 hour
What is the guideline for selecting the type of restraint to be used for a patient?	Use the least restrictive method that provides safety.
To which part of the bed should the restraints be tied?	To the bed frame, not the siderails.
In which type of knot should restraints be tied?	In a quick release slip knot.

How frequent do restraint orders need to be renewed?	In adults, restraint orders must be renewed every 24 hours. Medical reevaluation occurs much more frequently (every 4 hours).

SPREAD OF MICRO-ORGANISMS

Antibiotic (Define)	A drug that destroys or inhibits growth of micro-organisms.
Asepsis (Define)	Absence of organisms causing disease.
Antiseptic (Define)	A substance used to destroy or inhibit the growth of pathogens but not necessarily their spores (in general safe to use on persons).
Disinfectant (Define)	A substance used to destroy pathogens but not necessarily their spores (in general not intended for use on persons).
Bactericide (Define)	Substance capable of destroying microorganisms but not necessarily their spores.
Bacteriostatic (Define)	Substance that prevents or inhibits the growth of micro-organisms.
Anaerobe (Define)	Micro-organisms that do not require free oxygen to live.
Aerobe (Define)	Micro-organisms requiring free oxygen to live.
Pathogen (Define)	Micro-organism that causes disease.
Clean technique (Define)	Practices that help reduce the number and spread of micro-organisms (synonym for medical asepsis).
Sterile (Define)	An item on which all micro-organisms have been destroyed.
Coagulate (Define)	Process that thickens or congeals a substance.

Host (Define)	An animal or a person upon which or in which micro-organisms live.
Portal of entry (Define)	Part of the body where organisms enter.
Contaminate (Define)	To make something unclean or unsterile.
Surgical asepsis (Define)	Practices that render and keep objects and areas free from all micro-organisms (synonym for sterile techniques).
Medical asepsis (Define)	Practices that help reduce the number and spread of micro-organisms (synonym for clean techniques).
Spore (Define)	A cell produced by a micro-organism which develops into active micro-organisms under proper conditions.

CHAPTER 3
HEALTH PROMOTION & MAINTENANCE

ABRUPTIO PLACENTA

In Abruptio Placenta, the placenta ____ from the uterine wall ____.	Separates, prematurely
Abruptio Placenta usually occurs in (prima/multi) gravida over the age of ___.	Multigravida, 35 (HTN, trauma, cocaine are risk factors)
How is the bleeding of Abruptio Placenta different from that in Placenta Previa?	Usually with pain in Abruptio but not in Placenta Previa, bleeding more voluminous in Previa (the one that bleeds more has less pain; the one that bleeds less has more pain)
If you are the nurse starting the IV on the client with Abruptio Placenta, what gauge needle should you use?	18 gauge – to give blood if necessary
How often should you measure the vital signs, vaginal bleeding, fetal heart rate during Abruptio Placenta?	q 5-15 minutes for bleeding and maternal VS – continuous fetal monitoring, deliver at earliest sign of fetal distress (vital signs every 15 minutes is standard for unstable patients)
How is an infant delivered when Abruptio Placenta is present?	Usually, C-section
Is there a higher or lower incidence of fetal death with Abruptio Placenta compared to Placenta Previa?	Higher
In what trimester does Abruptio Placenta most commonly occur?	Third

ADULT DEVELOPMENT

What are the three adult stages of development called?	Early (young) adulthood, middle adulthood, later adulthood
What is the age range for young (early) adulthood?	19 to 35 years of age
What is the age range for middle adulthood?	35 to 65 years of age

What is the age range for late adulthood?	65 years of age to death
What is the developmental task for early adulthood?	Intimacy vs. Isolation
What is the developmental task for middle adulthood?	Generativity vs. Stagnation
What is the developmental task for later adulthood?	Ego integrity vs. Despair
"Time is too short to start another life, although I wish I could," is an example of ___.	Despair
"If I had to do it over again, I'd live my life just about the same," is an example of ____.	Ego integrity

APGAR SCALE

	0	1	2
Heart rate	absent	Slow, <100	>100
Respiratory effort	Absent	Slow, irregular	Vigorous cry
Muscle tone	Limp/flaccid	Flexion of extremities	Active motion
Reflex irritability	No response	Grimace	Cry
Color	Blue/pale	Pink body, blue extremities	Totally pink

APGAR SCORING

What is the APGAR scale?	It is a quick objective method to comparatively evaluate the VITAL FUNCTIONS of the newborn.
When is APGAR scoring performed on infants?	At one minute and again at 5 minutes after birth.
Name the 5 criteria that are recorded on an APGAR scale.	Cardiac status, respiratory effort, muscle tone, neuromuscular irritability (reflexes), and color.
The total APGAR score can range from __ to __.	0 to 10

The maximum score an infant can receive on any one criterion of the APGAR is ___.	2
The lowest score an infant can receive on any one criterion of the APGAR is __.	0
A 10 on the APGAR means the baby is _____.	In excellent health.
A 0 on the APGAR is ____ (bad/good).	Bad, the baby is stillborn
On heart rate or cardiac status, a 2 means that the HR is (above/below) ___ beats per minute.	Above, 100
On the heart rate criteria an infant score a "1" if their HR is (greater/lesser) than 0 but less than ____.	Greater, 100
In order to score a 0 on HR the infant must have a rate of ___.	Zero
A high score of 2 is given for the respiratory effort if the newborn _____ _____.	Cries vigorously
An infant is given a score of 1 if their respirations are _____ or _____.	Slow, irregular
An infant is given a score of 0 for respiratory effort if _____.	They do not breathe.
In order to get a score of 2 on muscle tone the infant must ____ _____.	Move spontaneously (actively)
To get a score of 1 on the APGAR for muscle tone the newborn must place their extremities in _____.	Flexion
A newborn receives a score of 0 on muscle tone when there is _____.	No movement (limp)
To score the maximum of 2 points on neuromuscular reflex irritability the infant must ____.	Cry

If the neonate _____, they will score a 1 on neuromuscular irritability.	Grimaces
To receive a 0 on reflex (neuromuscular irritability) the neonate must exhibit _____.	No response
To score a maximum score of 2 on color the child must be _____ _____.	Totally pink
If the child's _____ are _____ and the trunk-face-abdomen are _____, the child scores a 1 on color.	Extremities are blue (cyanotic), Pink
To get a 0 on color the infant is _____/_____.	Totally blue, pale
When a healthy child receives a 9 on the APGAR, they most likely get a 1 on _____.	Color, most healthy babies have acrocyanosis on the 1-minute APGAR but gets a 10 on the 5 minute. (Acrocyanosis is blue extremities, pink body)

BREASTFEEDING

With what solution and when should a breastfeeding mother cleanse the areola?	Plain water, before and after each feeding.
For a woman who doesn't have retracted nipples, is towel drying or air drying better?	Air drying of the nipples is best
The goal is for the infant to breast-feed for _____ minutes per side.	20 minutes
How does the mother break the suction of the BREASTFEEDING infant to be burped?	Place a finger into the side of the infant's mouth
Assuming no mastitis, on which side should BREAST FEEDING begin?	Begin nursing on the side that the baby finished on the last feeding
How long can breast milk be refrigerated?	24 hours
How long can breast milk be frozen?	6 months

In what type of container should breast milk be stored?	Sealed plastic bags
Can you microwave frozen breast milk in order to warm/thaw it?	Never
Which two nutrients is breast milk lower in?	Fluoride and iron
What should you tell a breastfeeding mother about her milk supply when she goes home from the hospital?	Milk should come in by postpartum day 3. Breastfeed every 2-3 hours to establish a good milk supply.
Can a woman on oral contraceptives breastfeed?	Should not use OCP during the first 6 weeks after birth because the hormones may decrease milk supply. Estrogen is not recommended. Non-hormonal methods are recommended. Remember breastfeeding is an unreliable contraceptive.

CARDIOVASCULAR DISEASE IN PREGNANCY-CD

CD ranks _____ among the leading causes of maternal death.	Fourth
What is the #1 cause of CD of pregnancy?	Rheumatic heart disease
Pregnancy requires a _____ increase in the cardiac output.	30-50%
What is the #1 cause of maternal death in CD of pregnancy?	Decompensation
What is meant by decompensation?	Failure of the heart to maintain adequate circulation.
What will you see when you observe the neck of a client with CD of pregnancy?	Distended neck veins-JVD
What will you hear when you auscultate the heart of the client with CD of pregnancy?	Murmurs

What will you hear when you auscultate the lungs of the client with CD of pregnancy?	Crackles-rales
If the client with CD of pregnancy experiences sudden heart failure what is the MOST common thing you will see?	Sudden onset of shortness of breath-dyspnea
What is the #1 treatment of CD during pregnancy?	Rest
What are the three most common drugs given to women with CD in pregnancy?	Diuretics, Heparin, Digitalis
Why are diuretics given to women with CD of pregnancy?	To promote diuresis, which will lower circulation blood volume, decrease preload, decrease the amount of blood the heart pumps.
Why are anticoagulants (heparin only) given to women with CD of pregnancy?	To prevent thrombophlebitis due to venous congestion, usually in legs.
Why is digitalis given to women with CD of pregnancy?	To increase the strength of the heart and to decrease the rate, rests the heart while making it more efficient.
Can a woman with CD of pregnancy be given analgesics during labor?	Yes, in fact they should be given analgesics, they may get too anxious which is bad for the heart.
What is the most common dietary modification for the woman with CD who shows signs of decompensation?	Decreased sodium, decreased water (restriction)
Is a C-section mandatory for delivery of a woman with CD of pregnancy?	No
Second to rest, what is a very important treatment for CD of pregnancy?	Weight control
How long must the woman with CD of pregnancy be on bed rest after delivery?	At least one week

What nutrients should be supplied in the diet of this woman?	Iron, folic acid, prevent anemia (anemia always makes the heart work more).
What are the two most common subjective complaints of the woman who is decompensating during labor?	SOB, palpitations
In addition to what you assess for in every woman during labor, what additional assessment must you make for a woman with CD?	You must assess lung sounds frequently
How often must you assess the lung sounds during the first stage of labor? During active labor? During transition labor?	Every 30 to 10 minutes
In which position should a woman with CD labor be?	Semi recumbent, HOB up
The nurse should limit the client's efforts to _____ _____ during labor when CD is present.	Bear down

CHILD'S RESPONSES TO PAIN AND ILLNESS

The infant fears _____ most when hospitalized.	Separation from love object
The toddler fears _____ most when hospitalized.	Separation from family
The preschooler fears separation as well as _____ when hospitalized.	Mutilation-remember preschoolers have vivid imaginations...fantasy
The toddler and preschooler will think that illness is caused by _____.	Something they did wrong.
The school-aged, hospitalized child is afraid of separation from _____.	Age group
The school-aged child perceives the cause of illness to be external or internal?	External, they know that illness is not a result of bad behavior.
The adolescent who is hospitalized fears separation from _____ and loss of _____.	Peers, independence

Preschoolers may require physical restraint during painful procedures. (T/F)	TRUE
Which age group engages in stalling tactics before painful procedures most?	School-Age
Which age groups are most likely to physically resist the nurse during procedures?	School-age, Adolescents
Toddlers may require physical restraint for painful procedures. (T/F)	TRUE

DANGERS VS. DISCOMFORTS IN PREGNANCY

First Trimester:

Developmental task: accepting fact of pregnancy "I am pregnant."

- Increased leukorrhea (normal within vaginal secretions)
- Nasal stuffiness
- Urinary frequency begins
- Fatigue
- Epistaxis (nose bleeds)
- Nausea and vomiting
- Breast changes (tenderness-pain-tingling-fullness)
- Ptyalism (perceived increase in salivation)
- Gingivitis

Second Trimester:

Developmental Task: accepting growing fetus as distinct from self and as a person to nurture, "I am going to have a baby"

- Heartburn
- Striae gravidarum
- Linea nigra
- Urinary frequency lessens
- Pruritis
- Joint pain and joint mobility
- Pelvic pressure
- Pigmentation deepens (areola, vulva)
- Palmar erythema

- Chloasma "mask of pregnancy" (Begins after week 16 and increases until delivery) • Supine hypotension (when supine, weight of the uterus presses against inferior vena cava, decreasing blood return to the heart, leading to decreased cardiac output.
- Hemorrhoids
- Backache
- Varicose veins appear
- Round ligament pain
- Carpal tunnel syndrome
- Oily skin and acne
- Constipation
- Palpitations
- Headaches
- Faintness
- Food cravings
- Pica (craving non-food items such as starch, dirt, clay)"

Third Trimester:

Developmental Task: preparing realistically for birth and parenting; "I am going to be a mother"

Pregnant woman fears possible defects in the baby

Pregnant woman fears labor and delivery--possible mutilation, pain, loss of control • Shortness of breath and dyspnea

- Urinary frequency returns
- Insomnia
- Braxton-Hicks contractions
- Ankle edema (non-pitting)
- Leg cramps
- Perineal pressure

Others:

- Mood swings--common throughout pregnancy
- Ambivalence (mixed feelings regarding pregnancy, labor and delivery, parenting, etc.) --all three trimesters
- Spider nevi appear over neck, thorax, face arms--2nd or 3rd trimester"

DANGER SIGNS

- Severe headaches
- Urinary tract infection (may lead to infection of fetal membranes and premature labor) • Epigastric pain (signals impending convulsion [pre-eclamptic])
- Severe abdominal pain
- Seizures
- Decreased fetal movements or absent fetal movement

- Fetal movements first felt around week 16 to 20, any change of pattern or abrupt cessation of fetal movement is ominous.
- Blurry vision (sign of preeclampsia)
- Vaginal bleeding
- Persistent, severe vomiting (can lead to dehydration and electrolyte imbalance)
- Edema of face or fingers (possible hypertension, pre-eclampsia)"

DEVELOPMENTAL MILESTONES

When does the anterior fontanel close?	18 to 24 months
Infant's birthweight should _ in 6 months.	Double
Infant's birth weight should_____ in one year.	Triple
Infant respiratory rate is_____to _____ breaths per minute.	30 to 60
Infant heart rate is _____to ____per minute.	110 to 160
Which are the first teeth to erupt?	Lower central incisors
When does an infant's teeth first erupt?	4 to 6 months
What age can an infant follow an object with its head?	2 months
What age are children first afraid of strangers?	6 to 7 months
What age does an infant walk alone?	14 to 15 months
What age does an infant have a pincer grasp?	12 to 13 months
What age can an infant roll over?	4 to 5 months
At what age can an infant sit up unassisted?	6 to 8 months
What age does an infant stand alone?	12 to 13 months

What age does an infant crawl?	8 to 9 months
What age does an infant walk holding onto furniture?	10 to 11 months

ECTOPIC PREGNANCY

Ectopic pregnancy is implantation of a fertilized ovum _____ the _____.	Outside, uterus
The most common site for ectopic pregnancy is in the _____ _____.	Fallopian tube--90%
Have intrauterine devices to prevent pregnancy ever been linked to ectopic pregnancy?	Yes, so have pelvic infections.
What is the most common sign of fallopian tube ectopic pregnancy?	Unilateral pelvic pain
What is the most dangerous side effect/ complication of fallopian ectopic pregnancy?	Rupture of the fallopian tube
If the fallopian tube ruptures due to ectopic pregnancy, nursing care is the same as that for _____.	Shock and peritonitis
The uterus feels _____ after rupture of a fallopian ectopic pregnancy.	Boggy--tender, also
The first sign that a fallopian ectopic pregnancy had ruptured is...	Sharp abdominal pain
Ectopic pregnancy is (usually/almost never) carried to term.	Almost never
The most common medical-surgical treatment for ectopic pregnancy is _____.	Surgical removal of fetus and some surrounding tissue

Name the surgery performed for ectopic pregnancy.	Exploratory laparotomy

ELIMINATION: BOWEL (GENERAL)

What will excessively fatty stool be like?	Large, pale, foul-smelling, greasy.
What are large, pale, foul-smelling, greasy stools called?	Steatorrhea
Name three types of parasites abnormally found in stool.	Roundworm, tapeworm, pinworm
What does occult blood in feces mean?	Bleeding somewhere in the GI tract
Are fats a normal constituent of feces?	Yes, but it should be WNL (within normal limits).
A decrease in urobilin in stool results in a stool that is _____ _____.	Clay-colored
Name two things for which stool specimens are tested.	Occult blood, fat, ova and parasites
Is blood a normal constituent of feces?	No
What is melena?	A black, tarry stool indicating a GI bleed.

ENDOMETRIOSIS

What is endometriosis?	Growth of endometrial tissue outside of the uterus.
Endometriosis most commonly occurs in women between ages of _____ and _____.	25 to 40
After menopause, endometriosis (decreases/ increases).	Decreases
What is the MOST common symptom of endometriosis?	Dysmenorrhea, painful menstruation

What is the major complication of endometriosis?	Infertility
What diagnostic procedure confirms the diagnosis of endometriosis?	Laparoscopy
What class of drug is used to conservatively treat endometriosis?	Androgens
Which androgen drug is most used to treat endometriosis?	Danazol
Women with endometriosis should be counseled to use (tampons/pads) during menstruation?	Pads only
Will the client die of endometriosis? What would you say?	Not life-threatening
What advice is best for women with endometriosis who want to have children?	Do not postpone pregnancy, may not be able to have children.

ERIKSON'S STAGES OF PSYCHOSOCIAL DEVELOPMENT

Match the stage name with the correct facts about it: adolescents, school-age, preschooler, toddler, infancy, and young adulthood.

Autonomy vs. Shame and doubt	Toddler
Industry vs. Inferiority	School age
18 to 25 years	Young adult
Says "no"	Toddler
Encourage creativity and collecting things	School age
Give choices	Toddler
Centers on having basic needs met	Infancy

18 months to 3 years	Toddler
3 to 6 years	Pre-schooler
12 to 20 years	Adolescent
Initiative vs. Guilt	Pre-schooler
6 to 12 years old	School age
Trust vs. Mistrust	Infancy
Peer group important	Adolescent
Encourage fantasy	Pre-schooler
Identity vs. Role confusion	Adolescent
Intimacy vs. Isolation	Young adult
Birth to 18 months	Infancy

GROWTH & DEVELOPMENT

The sequence of growth and development is predictable. (T/F)	TRUE
The rate of growth and development is even. (T/F?)	False, it goes in spurts and is often very uneven
Growth and development are a pediatric concern only. (T/F)	FALSE
Heredity determines most growth. (T/F)	TRUE
Environment determines most development. (T/F)	TRUE

The rate a person grows and develops is predictable. (T/F)	False, the sequence is more predictable than the rate.
Heredity has no influence on development. (T/F)	False, it is a secondary influence (it is not the primary influence--environment is)
The heart is a (fast/slow) growing organ.	Slow
Which component of growth and development is predictable: time of onset, length of stage, effect of stage, and sequence of stage?	Sequence
What is meant by the phrase--Growth and Development is cephalocaudal?	Growth and development starts with the head and moves to the extremities.
Growth and development occurs first in _____ body parts and progresses to _____ body parts.	Proximal, distal
In which phase is rate of growth most rapid-- infancy or adolescence?	Infancy
The proportion of the body that is water (rises/ falls) with age?	Falls, in infants is 70% water and adult is 58%.
An infant's stomach is (more/less) acid than adults.	Less
Lymphoid tissue mass grows steadily throughout life. (T/F)	False, it decreases in mass after adolescence.
An adult's height begins to decline after the average age of _____.	30
The brain is fully mature in size at birth. (T/F)	False, but by the end of the first year of life you will have all the brain cells you will ever have.
By what age do most children have all their deciduous teeth?	End of the 2nd year of life

HEALTH PROMOTION

What information does measurement of skinfold thickness yield?	The amount of body fat.

In general, males have a higher risk of heart disease than females. (T/F)	TRUE
Post-menopausal females have a lower risk of heart disease than males aged 25 to 40. (T/F)	False. They have a higher risk.
Family history of diabetes increases the risk of heart disease. (T/F)	TRUE
Family history of liver disease increases the risk of heart disease. (T/F)	FALSE
Cigarette smoking increases the risk of heart disease. (T/F)	TRUE
Oral contraceptives decrease the risk of heart disease. (T/F)	False, use increases the risk.
Routine exercise decreases the risk of heart disease. (T/F)	TRUE

HYPEREMESIS GRAVIDARUM

Hyperemesis gravidarum is _____ and _____ vomiting that persists into the _____ trimester.	Severe and prolonged; 2nd trimester (normal vomiting should be gone before 2nd trimester).
Give three possible causes of hyperemesis gravidarum.	Pancreatitis, multiple pregnancy, hydatidiform mole.
Has hyperemesis gravidarum ever been associated with mixed feelings about pregnancy?	Yes, increased incidence of it in women who are ambivalent about pregnancy.
What are the two most common complications of hyperemesis gravidarum?	Electrolyte imbalance (dehydration), starvation.
What is the initial diet order for clients with hyperemesis gravidarum?	NPO
Why are doctors cautious in using antiemetics to treat hyperemesis gravidarum?	They don't want to harm the fetus.

What are the instructions given to clients recovering from hyperemesis gravidarum in relation to mealtime?	Remain seated upright for 45 minutes after each meal.
What is the biggest challenge in nursing care of the client with hyperemesis gravidarum?	Getting them to eat.

MASTITIS AND BREAST ENGORGEMENT

Mastitis and breast engorgement are more likely to occur in (primipara/multipara).	Primipara
Where does the organism that causes mastitis come from?	The infant's nose or mouth.
Which organism most commonly causes mastitis?	Staph
Prolonged intervals between breast-feeding (decrease/increase) the incidence of mastitis.	Increase
Can too-tight bras lead to mastitis?	Yes, by preventing emptying of ducts.
Mastitis usually occurs at least _____ days after delivery.	10
When mastitis is present the breasts are _____, _____, and _____.	Hard, swollen, warm
Mastitis is accompanied by a fever over _____.	102°
If mastitis is caused by an organism, what causes breast engorgement?	Temporary increase in vascular & lymph supply to the breast in preparation for milk production.
If mastitis occurs 1+ weeks after delivery, when does breast engorgement occur?	2 to 5 days after delivery
Does breast engorgement interfere with nursing?	Yes, the infant has a difficult time latching on (getting nipple in its mouth).
What class of drugs is used to treat mastitis?	Antibiotics

Antibiotics are used to treat breast engorgement. (T/F)	FALSE
Application of (warm H2O compresses/ice packs) is the preferred treatment for breast engorgement.	Ice packs to decrease swelling.
The mother with mastitis should stop breastfeeding. (T/F)	False, the mother must keep breast feeding. (Offer unaffected breast first.)
If the mother has an open abscess on her breast, she must not breast-feed. (T/F)	TRUE
For breast engorgement, the non-breastfeeding mother should be told to express breast milk (T/F)	No, that would increase milk production and would make the problem worse (warm compresses or a warm shower to let milk "leak" is okay--Ice is best).
What is the best treatment for breast engorgement?	Breast feeding--it will balance supply and demand.

MENSTRUATION AND OVARIAN CYCLE

Average duration of menstrual flow is _____. The normal range is _____ to _____ days.	5 days, 3 to 6
Average blood loss during menstruation is _____ mL.	50 to 60 mL
Name the two phases of the ovarian cycle.	Follicular phase (first 14 days), luteal phase (Second 14 days)
In the menstrual cycle, day 1 is the day on which....	Menstrual discharge begins
How long does an ovarian cycle last?	Average of 28 days
How many days after ovulation does menstruation begin?	14 days
What hormones are active during the follicular phase?	FSH and Estrogen

During the luteal phase of the ovarian cycle which of the following hormones increase: estrogen, progesterone, or LH?	Progesterone and LH
What is the major function of the luteal phase of the ovarian cycle?	To develop and maintain the corpus luteum which produces progesterone to maintain pregnancy until placenta is established.
If an ovum is fertilized during the luteal phase what hormone will be secreted?	HCG (human chorionic gonadotropin)
During menstruation, the average daily loss of iron is _____ mg.	0.5 to 1.0 mg
What occurs during the follicular phase of the ovarian cycle?	It accomplishes maturation of the graafian follicle which results in ovulation.

NEUROLOGICAL EXAMINATION

Name the three sub-scales in the Glasgow coma scale (GCS).	Best eye opening (E), Best verbal response (V), and best motor response (M)
What is the maximum score on the GCS?	15
What is the minimum score on the GCS?	3
A score equal to or below _____ on the GCS is considered a coma.	7
Pupillary reaction tests cranial nerve #_____.	3
A respiratory pattern in which there is alternation between apnea and hyperventilation is known as...	Cheyne-Stokes
A value of 20/80 on visual acuity means that the patient can see at _____ feet what normal people see at _____ feet.	20, 80
Babinski's reflex is tested by stroking the _____.	Bottom lateral surface of the foot.

It is always pathologic if a Babinski is negative. (T/F)	False, non-walking infants normally have a positive Babinski, walking infants, toddlers and all other should normally have a negative Babinski.
When a Babinski is positive the _____ _____ _____ flexes and the other _____ fan out.	Great toe dorsiflexes, toes
In decorticate posturing, the legs are _____ and the neck and arms are _____ and _____ rotated.	Extended, flexed, internally
In decerebrate posturing, the legs are _____ and the arms, neck, and back are _____.	Extended, extended (pronated).
A score of 4 for a reflex means that it is _____.	Hyperactive
Cerebellar function is evaluated by testing for _____, _____, _____, _____.	Posture, gait, balance, coordination (ie, Romberg's Sign)

ORAL CONTRACEPTIVES

What are the two types of oral contraceptives?	Progestin only & combination progesterone and estrogen.
How many days of the menstrual cycle do you take the progestin only pill?	All 28 days.
How many days of the menstrual cycle do you take the combination pill?	You take it on days 5-24, but not on days 2428 and 1-4 (8 days off).
How long before surgery must you discontinue oral contraceptives?	One week before surgery.
If a woman forgets to take the pill one day, what should she do?	Take it as soon as she remembers it and take the next pill at regular time.
What if a woman forgets to take the pill for two days in a row? What should she do?	Take 2 pills a day for two days in a row and then resume normal schedule.
What should a woman do if she forgets to take her pill for 3 days or more?	Throw away packs & start new packs the same day. Use a back-up contraceptive method for 7 days.

If a woman doesn't stop oral contraceptives one week before surgery, she is at risk for developing _____.	Thrombophlebitis
People who smoke more than _____ cigarettes per day should not be on oral contraceptives.	15, because if you smoke you have constriction of vessels and this potentates the chances that a woman on oral contraceptives will get thrombophlebitis.
If a woman on oral contraceptives misses a period, should she still take pills?	Yes, however if 2 missed periods occur, stop, and have a pregnancy test.
Will breakthrough bleeding, nausea and vomiting and breast tenderness go away when a woman is on oral contraceptives?	Yes, after about 3-6 months of treatment.

OVERVIEW OF LABOR & DELIVERY

What does lightening mean?	When the fetal head descends into the pelvis.
When does it occur in pregnancy?	2-3 weeks before birth for primip
What is the most common positive effect of lightening?	After it occurs the woman can breathe much easier.
Name the two earliest signs that a woman is likely in labor.	Low back pain and show (blood-tinged mucous plug is passed)
What is the most RELIABLE or VALID indication that a woman is in labor?	The onset of regular contractions that result in progressive dilatation/effacement of the cervix.
What are the 2 processes that occur to the cervix during labor?	Effacement and dilation
What is the meaning of cervical effacement?	The cervix thins.
Into how many stages is labor and delivery divided?	4
What is accomplished during the first stage of labor and delivery?	Full effacement and dilation

How long is the first stage of labor and delivery for a primagravida? For a multigravida?	12 hours, 6 hours
The cervix is fully dilated when it is_____ cm.	10
The 2nd stage of labor and delivery accomplishes...	Delivery of the infant
The 2nd stage of labor and delivery begins with _____ and ends with _____ of the _____.	Full dilation, delivery, infant
The 2nd stage of labor and delivery lasts _____ hour(s) for a primagravida and _____ hour(s) for a multigravida.	1 ½ hours, ½ hour
The 3rd stage of labor and delivery accomplishes...	Expulsion of the placenta.
The 3rd stage of labor and delivery lasts...	Less than one hour
What occurs during the 4th stage of labor and delivery?	Recovery
When does the 4th stage of labor and delivery end?	2 hours after expulsion of the placenta
What is the average blood loss during labor?	500 mL
When the terminology "the three phases of labor" is used, what does it mean?	If the statement refers to phases of labor, it means the 3-step process of latency, followed by active and transitional.

OVERVIEW OF PREGNANCY

Normal length of pregnancy is _____ to _____ days.	240, 300
Pregnancy is divided into _____ trimesters.	3
During the first trimester the woman experiences decreased or increased vaginal secretions?	Increased

When are urine pregnancy tests positive?	At the time of the first missed period.
Pregnancy tests test for the presence of what hormone?	HCG (human chorionic gonadotropin hormone)
Urine and blood pregnancy tests are enough evidence to be certain of pregnancy. (T/F?)	False, these tests only suggest pregnancy.
What is Hegar's sign?	Uterine softening
What is Chadwick's sign?	Blue tint to the cervix
The first trimester goes from week _____ to _____ week .	1, 13
The second trimester goes from week _____ to week _____.	14, 27
Which week can mother first feel the fetus move?	16th to 20th week, (the end of the 4th month into the 5th month)
What is the word used to identify the feeling that the mother experiences when the fetus moves?	Quickening
The 3rd trimester goes from week _____ to week _____.	28, 40
In which trimester does the woman most feel backache?	Third
Which trimester is the fetus most susceptible to effects of outside agents?	First
What is the name of the process in which outside agents cause birth defect in the fetus?	Teratogenesis
Which trimester is nausea and vomiting most common?	First
Which trimester do Braxton-Hicks contractions begin?	Third

What are Braxton-Hicks?	Usually, painless contractions that strengthen the uterus for labor.
Which trimester does quickening occur?	Second
Which trimester does venous congestion in the legs occur?	Third
Which trimester does linea nigra appear?	Second
What is linea nigra?	Single dark vertical line on the abdomen.
Which trimester do striations occur?	Second
What are striations?	Horizontal pigmented lines on the abdomen
What is chloasma?	Mask of pregnancy-pigmented area on the face.
Which trimester is constipation most common?	Third

PIAGET AND INTELLECTUAL DEVELOPMENT

What is conservation? In what stage does it develop?	When the child realizes that number, weight, volume remain the same even when outward appearances change; Concrete Operational.
What is the age range of formal operational thinking?	12 to 15
What is the sensorimotor stage of intellectual development?	It is the intellectual stage of children from birth to 2 years.
What is the age range of concrete operational thinking?	7 to 11
What is the age range of preoperational thinking?	3 to 6
What is the classic pattern in formal operational thinking?	Abstract reasoning
What is egocentricity? In what stage is it found?	The child views everything from his frame of reference, common in pre-operational thinking.

PLACENTA PREVIA

In Placenta Previa the placenta is implanted _____ than it should be and lays over the _____ _____.	Lower, cervical os
What is the classic symptom of Placenta Previa?	Painless 3rd trimester bleeding (hint: Painless Placenta Previa)
In whom is Placenta Previa most likely to occur? Primagravida's or multigravida's?	Multigravida's
What is meant when the physician/nurse use the terms total (complete) or partial (incomplete) in reference to placenta previa?	Total or complete: placenta covers the whole cervical opening. Partial or incomplete: placenta covers only part of the cervical opening.
What are the 3 complications of placenta previa?	Shock, maternal death, fetal death
What is the best and safest way to confirm placenta previa?	Ultrasound
Should a woman with Placenta Previa be hospitalized?	Yes, always if bleeding.
If a surgeon delays doing a C-section for Placenta Previa it is due to: (reason for delay).	Immaturity of the fetus (they will want the child to mature)
As soon as Placenta Previa is diagnosed, most pregnancies will be terminated via C-section if the fetus is mature. (T/F?)	TRUE
If a woman is admitted with active bleeding with Placenta Previa, you should monitor fetal heart tones _____ .	Continuously via fetal monitor
It is not necessary to use electronic fetal monitoring when there is active bleeding in Placenta Previa. (T/F?)	False, infants must always be monitored.
Will a woman with active bleeding in Placenta Previa be given any systemic pain relief during labor?	No, they don't want to depress the fetus.

If you were told to start the IV on the woman admitted for Placenta Previa, what gauge needle would you use?	18 gauge, or any other one large enough to administer blood.

PREGNANCY AND DIABETES

Pregnancy (decreases/increases) the body's insulin requirements.	Increases
Can pregnancy convert a non-diabetic woman into a diabetic?	Yes
What name is given to diabetes that is brought on by pregnancy?	Gestational diabetes
Diabetes with pregnancy is (more/less) common as the woman ages.	More
What is the #1 cause of infant illness when the mother has diabetes?	Hypoglycemia
When is infant hypoglycemia most likely to occur during labor and delivery?	In the hours immediately following delivery.
Hormones of pregnancy work against insulin. (T/F)	TRUE
A sign of gestational diabetes is excessive (weight gain/weight loss).	Weight gain
(Obese/very thin) women are most likely to become diabetic during pregnancy.	Obese
In gestational diabetes the client experiences a (decrease/increase) in thirst.	Increase (polydipsia)
In gestational diabetes the client experiences a (decrease/increase) in urine output.	Increase (polyuria)
Gestational diabetes is associated with (hypertension/hypotension).	Hypertension

Gestational diabetes is associated with what OB history?	Previous large baby (over 9 lb), unexplained stillbirth, miscarriage, congenital anomalies
Women who have gestational diabetes tend to deliver infants who are (small/large).	Large for gestational age
Gestational diabetics tend to get _____ infections.	Monilial (yeast) infections
What test confirms the diagnoses of gestational diabetes?	3-hour glucose tolerance test
What are the two main treatment methods in gestational diabetes?	Diet, insulin
How often should a woman visit the doctor prenatally if diabetes is present?	Twice a month, then once per week in the 3rd trimester.
How many pounds per week is the diabetic allowed to gain the 2nd and 3rd trimesters?	1 pound a week
Is severe carbohydrate restriction required in gestational diabetics?	No, it could lead to ketosis
Of protein, fat, and carbohydrates, which ones (percentwise) increase in the diet of gestational diabetes?	Protein, fat
When is insulin used in the treatment of gestational diabetes?	When dietary control does not keep the blood sugar within normal limits.
If insulin is used, the dose is the same in all 3 trimesters. (T/F)	False, it varies
Oral hypoglycemics should never be used during pregnancy. (T/F)	True, they cause birth defects (teratogenic).
When should a diabetic be delivered?	Between 37 and 39 weeks
What IV solution is used during labor for the diabetic?	D5W

The mother's insulin requirements will (fall/rise) markedly after delivery.	Fall
During pregnancy what complication is most dangerous for the fetus of a diabetic?	Ketosis
If ketosis is a big problem for the baby during pregnancy what is the big problem after delivery?	Hypoglycemia
Why is hypoglycemia such a dangerous problem?	Brain cells die without glucose, brain damage

PREGNANCY-INDUCED HYPERTENSION—PIH

(Multi/prima) gravida clients are most likely to get PIH.	Primigravida
Which age group(s) are most likely to experience PIH?	Patients under 18 or over 35
When does pre-eclampsia usually begin in pregnancy (week)?	After 20 weeks
Name the three symptoms of PIH.	Hypertension, weight gain (edema), proteinuria
If preeclampsia is mild will the woman be hospitalized?	No, just rest at home
What type of diet is indicated for a woman with preeclampsia?	Increased protein / normal salt intake (no restriction typically)
What measurement must the woman with preeclampsia make every day?	She must weigh herself
What is the activity order for a woman with severe pre-eclampsia?	Bed rest
What is the best position for the client with severe pre-eclampsia?	Left side lying
What is the dietary order for the woman with severe pre-eclampsia?	Low salt, high protein

Are diuretics used for women with preeclampsia?	Yes
When a woman is hospitalized for severe pre-eclampsia, the nurse should test the....	#1-reflexes, the urine for protein
When preeclampsia gets worse the deep tendon reflexes will be (hyper/hypo) reflexia.	Hyper-reflexia
Pre-eclampsia makes the neuromuscular system (more or less) irritable?	More
What vision problem do women with preeclampsia have?	Blurred vision
What type of precautions will be in effect for a woman with severe pre-eclampsia?	Seizure precautions
Name 5 things included in seizure precautions	Suction machine in room, O2 in room, padded rails up x4, must stay on unit, ambulation with supervision only, no more than 1 pillow
When is preeclampsia called eclampsia?	Once convulsions have occurred
In an eclamptic client what ominous sign almost always precedes a seizure?	Severe epigastric pain
What are the three major treatment objectives in eclampsia?	Decrease blood pressure, control convulsions, diuresis
The urine output of the eclamptic client will (decrease/increase).	Decrease
How would you palpate the uterus to see if the eclamptic woman was having contractions?	Place the hand flat on the abdomen over the fundus with the fingers apart and press lightly.

PREMATURE RUPTURE OF MEMBRANES—PROM

Premature rupture of membranes (PROM) is a _____ break in the amniotic sac _____ the _____ of contractions.	Spontaneous, before, onset

Usually labor starts within _____ hours of rupture of membranes.	24
What is the danger with PROM?	Infection
How would you tell if the woman with PROM had an infection?	Maternal fever, fetal tachycardia, foul smelling vaginal discharge
To test for amniotic fluid the nurse should check the _____ of the fluid.	pH
Amniotic fluid is (acidic/alkaline)	Alkaline
Being alkaline means having a (high/low) pH?	High
Amniotic fluid turns nitrazine paper deep _____ (color).	Blue
When PROM occurs, the age of the fetus must be determined. The best way to assess lung maturity is to check the _____ ratio.	L/S (lecithin/sphingomyelin)
An L/S ratio greater than _____ indicates lung maturity.	2
If labor does not begin within _____ hours after PROM, labor will be induced.	24
If PROM occurs before viability, what is the typical management?	Termination of pregnancy
If PROM occurs after viability but before 36 weeks, what is the typical management?	Hospitalize, watch for infection, try to gain time for the infant to mature
If there are any signs of infection after PROM, what must occur immediately?	Delivery of the fetus
PROM always occurs in a gush of fluid. (T/F)	FALSE
The woman must avoid sexual intercourse if PROM has occurred. (T/F)	TRUE

SCREENING ASSESSMENTS

At what age should women begin annual mammography for breast cancer?	45 (Newer data suggests 40.)
When should screening for colon cancer begin if the risk is average?	45-50. American Cancer Society says 45.
When should screening for colon cancer continue until in healthy clients?	Up to age 75.
What two methods of colon cancer screening are recommended?	Stool based tests, colonoscopy.
How often should colonoscopies for colon cancer be performed?	Once every 10 years. Every 5 years if over 75 and increased risk.
At what age should screening for cervical cancer begin? Until what age?	25 65
What are the two screening tests for cervical cancer?	HPV testing, Pap test.
How often should HPV testing be performed?	Once every 5 years.
How often should Pap tests be performed?	Once every 3 years.
Do you need to do both?	No
At what age can screening for cervical cancer be stopped?	65
What test screens for lung cancer?	LDCT scans
What test screens for prostate cancer.	Prostate specific antigen test (PSA).
At what age is PSA testing recommended to begin?	Age 50, ...45 if strong family history

How often should a patient be screened for hypertension?	At yearly exam after 40. If cardiovascular disease start at 18.
How often should a person be screened for diabetes mellitus?	Yearly
When should diabetes screening begin?	At age 45.
What test screens for Diabetes?	The hemoglobin A1C. (HA1C)
What HA1C levels suggests PRE-diabetes?	Greater than or equal to 5.7 is PRE-diabetes. (Diabetes is greater than or equal to 6.5.)

THE FAMILY

Define nuclear family.	A family of parents and their offspring.
When does a nuclear family become an extended family?	When aunts or uncles or grandparents live with the family.
Give the 2 major roles of the family in society.	To protect and socialize.
What percentage of North American families are single parent?	50%
90% of single-parent families are headed by a _____.	Female
In what step of the nursing process does the nurse ask the family about their beliefs on illness?	Assessment phase
What is the first thing a nurse must do to help families in crisis?	Nurse must first examine their own values.

CHAPTER 4

PSYCHOSOCIAL INTEGRITY

ANOREXIA NERVOSA

Anorexics are usually _____ under the age of _____ .	Females, 25
The diagnosis is made when there is a weight loss of __% or more of body weight.	15% (Weigh <85% of normal body wt.) Hospitalize if 30% wt. loss
A major mental/emotional nursing diagnosis seen in anorexia nervosa is _____ .	Altered body image
The pulse rate of anorexics is tachycardic or bradycardic?	Bradycardic
List the most common gynecologic symptom of anorexia nervosa.	Amenorrhea
What is found over the body of the client with anorexia nervosa?	Lanugo – soft downy hair
What is the top priority in the care of the client with anorexia nervosa?	Intake of enough food to keep them alive, have them gain weight
The best goal to evaluate the progress of the client with anorexia nervosa is _____ .	An adequate weight gain

DEFENSE MECHANISMS

Purpose of defense mechanisms is to reduce _____ .	Anxiety
When a person is consciously choosing to disbelieve the truth, they are using _____ .	Denial
Defense mechanisms are always unhealthy. (T/F)	False, in fact defense mechanisms are often and most always healthy because they reduce anxiety.
When a patient hates someone, but then expresses the opposite emotion, it is called _____ .	Reaction formation--you form the opposite reaction, i.e., you love a person and that makes you anxious, so you form the opposite reaction, and you ignore them.

When an angry patient says, "I am not mad, he is"; they are using _____.	Projection
When a person is unconsciously choosing to disbelieve the truth, they are using _____.	Repression
When the patient makes an excuse about something bad that happened, they are _____.	Rationalizing
When a patient becomes demanding and self-centered and attention-seeking, the defense mechanism used is _____.	Regression
Defense mechanisms are ways to lie to yourself. (T/F)	True, they all involve self-deception.
When a patient tells all kinds of details about very upsetting events but acts very cool and calm, they are using _____.	Intellectualization
When a patient expresses their emotions toward another object they are using _____.	Displacement
The defense mechanism most suspected of causing psychosomatic illness is _____.	Repression

ELECTRO-SHOCK (CONVULSIVE) THERAPY—ECT

What is ECT?	The use of electrical shock current delivered to the brain to induce a seizure that treats depression.
The client is (awake/under local anesthesia/ under general anesthesia) during ECT.	Under general anesthesia--must be artificially ventilated.
What conditions does ECT treat?	Depression primarily
Is informed consent necessary for ECT?	Yes
Name the three most common complications of ECT.	Aspiration of emesis (most common) into the lung, dislocations of joints, fractures due to convulsion--rare today.

What class of drugs is given with ECT?	Muscle relaxant--succinylcholine
What intellectual ability is impaired after ECT?	Memory
How long will a client's memory be impaired after ECT?	Two to three weeks
Immediately after ECT, how will the client normally act?	Drowsy, dull, apathetic
In what position should the client be immediately after ECT?	On their side--to prevent aspiration
What typical pre-operative type of orders will be ordered before ECT?	NPO after midnight--remove dentures, client to void before surgery, side rails up.
The convulsion (seizure) that the electrical current produced is violent. (T/F)	False, it used to be, but it isn't any more with the use of muscle relaxants.

OBSESSIVE-COMPULSIVE DISORDER

Anxiety-producing thoughts are called _____.	Obsessions
Repetitive actions designed to reduce anxiety are called _____.	Compulsions--such as washing hands over and over, dusting furniture 3 hours per day, refusing to turn your back to anyone.
Which defense mechanism is most closely associated with obsessive-compulsive disorder?	Displacement
Should you allow an obsessive-compulsive person to perform their compulsive behavior?	Yes, give them time to do their ritual and try to set a limit and redirect.
Should you ever make an obsessive-compulsive person stop their compulsive behavior?	No, they will become very anxious.
Is the patient with obsessive-compulsive disorder non psychotic or psychotic?	Non psychotic, they know reality.
Should you confront the obsessive-compulsive patient with the absurdity of their behavior?	No, just say things like "You washed your hands for so long you must have been very anxious."

What should you do if an obsessive-compulsive patient is always late due to their rituals?	Get them started earlier--for example if they wash their hands for ½ hour before meals and are always late for breakfast, just get them started ½ hour earlier.

PSYCHOLOGY FOUNDATIONS

What is self-disclosure?	When the nurse tells the patient personal information about self.
Is it always bad for the nurse to self-disclose?	No, you can self-disclose as long as you do it cautiously and you are 100% sure it is therapeutic.
If the nurse uses self-disclosure, it should be _____ and the conversation should be....	Short, quickly refocused back on the patient
Insight means the ability of the patient to _____ their problem.	Understand
During what phase should the nurse examine his/her own feelings?	Pre-interaction phase
Flight of ideas is when the patient changes topics of conversation _____.	Rapidly
The basis for a therapeutic nurse/patient relationship begins with the _____ self- _____ and _____ _____.	Nurse's, awareness, self-understanding
What are the steps of the nurse/patient therapeutic relationship?	Pre-interaction phase, orientation phase, working phase, termination phase
Should the nurse self-disclose if the patient asks the nurse to?	No, not unless it is specifically therapeutic
The nurse should introduce information about the end of the nurse/patient relationship during the _____ phase.	Orientation phase
Termination phase begins in the _____ phase.	Orientation

RAPE TRAUMA SYNDROME

Rape is a crime of passion. (T/F)?	False, it is a violent act.
When must psychological care of the rape victim begin?	In the emergency room.
Name the two phases of Rape Trauma Syndrome.	Disorganization phase, re-organization phase
Immediately after rape, the person who is calm and composed is adjusting well. (T/F)?	False, calmness and a composed attitude are signs of Rape Trauma syndrome, (calm person is just as disorganized as the crying and upset person)
Name the 3 physical symptoms of Rape Trauma Syndrome.	GI irritability, itching or burning on urination, skeletal muscle tension, *don't forget PAIN
Victims of rape often blame _____.	Themselves
In the long-term reorganization phase the person is likely to change _____.	Residence or/and telephone number
In the long-term re-organization phase the victim is likely to experience _____ during sleep.	Nightmares
In the long-term re-organization phase the victim has four common fears. Name them . . .	1) Indoors or outdoors (depending on where the rape occurred) 2) Being alone or in crowds 3) People being behind them 4) Sexual fears
Before evidence from the victim's body can be gathered for rape, _____ _____ must be completed.	Consent forms
Should a same gender staff member be present when the rape victim is being examined?	Always
The rape victim requires only a pelvic exam, and a head-to-toe exam is not done, so the client is not stressed. (T/F)?	False, the exam is a very long, invasive head-to-toe exam.

During the exam, the vaginal speculum is lubricated before it is placed in the vagina. (T/F)?	False, lubrication could alter the evidence.
What drug is often used to prevent pregnancy after rape?	Kits approved by FDA: Preven (levonorgestrel & ethinyl estradiol) or Plan B: Levonorgestrel (less N&V)
When working with a rape victim they should be treated with _____ and _____.	Dignity and respect
After rape, a victim needs follow-up exam/test for _____ _____ _____.	Sexually transmitted diseases (STD's), i.e., AIDS, gonorrhea, syphilis . . .
After discharge contact with the rape victim is maintained via the _____.	Telephone

SUICIDE

Do you assess for suicide potential whenever a patient makes any statement about wanting to die or kill self?	Yes, in fact whenever a patient makes a statement about wishing or wanting to die or kill self you must **ALWAYS AND FIRST** assess for suicide potential--stop everything and assess for suicide patient (except CPR, of course).
Children are at _____ risk for suicide.	Low
Adolescents are (low/high) risk for suicide.	High
Young adults are (low/high) risk for suicide.	High to moderate
People between 25 and 50 years are (low/moderate/high) risk for suicide.	Low to moderate
People over 50 years are (low/high) risk for suicide.	High
The patient who has a definite plan is (low/high) risk for suicide.	Moderate to high, depends upon feasibility and ease of plan.
The use of pills makes the patient (low/ moderate/high) risk for suicide.	Moderate

The patient who has NO definite plan is (low/high) risk for suicide.	Low
The use of _____, _____ and _____ to kill self, make high risk suicide.	Guns, ropes, knives
Who is at higher risk for suicide, a man or a woman?	Man
Of: married, divorced, and separated, which marital status is highest risk for suicide? Lowest risk for suicide?	Highest-separated then divorced Lowest-married
The goal of action while the suicidal patient is still on the phone is to get _____ person _____ the _____.	Another person on the scene (this immediately decreases risk) Remember: people who are alone are always high risk.
What are the four classic suicide precautions?	Search personal belongings for drugs and alcohol, remove any sharp objects, remove any device for hanging or strangling; must be on constant one-to-one observation (NEVER out of sight).
Once the patient is admitted for attempted suicide should you ever discuss the attempt with them?	No, you should not focus on the attempt, focus on the present and future.

CHAPTER 5

Basic Care & Comfort

ACNE

What is the causative organism of acne?	P. acnes (Propionibacterium acnes)
What structures are involved in Acne Vulgaris?	The sebaceous glands
Name 3 drugs given for acne	Vitamin A, Antibiotics, Retinoids, Isotretinoin (Accutane)
Dietary indiscretions are a cause of acne (T/F)	FALSE
What are the 3 causative factors in Acne Vulgaris?	Heredity, Bacterial, Hormonal
Uncleanliness is a cause of acne (T/F)	FALSE
What is the most common retinoid given to people with acne?	Accutane
Accutane is an analog of which vitamin?	Vitamin A
What is the most common side effect of Accutane?	Inflammation of the lips
What side effect is MOST important in health teaching in Accutane administration?	It can cause birth defects
What is the antibiotic most given to clients with acne?	Tetracycline
How long will it take for the person to see results when acne is being treated?	4 to 6 weeks
Does stress make acne worse?	Yes
How often should the client with acne wash his face each day?	Twice a day
What instructions do you give to a client taking tetracycline?	Take it on an empty stomach and avoid the sunlight (photosensitivity)
What are comedones?	Blackheads and white heads

ACTIVITIES OF DAILY LIVING—ADL

What are the two **categories** of ADL's?	Basic ADL's and Institutional ADL's
What are basic ADLs?	Activities a healthy person performs in physical self-care.
What are some examples of basic ADLs	Eating, hygiene, ambulating, toileting, dressing, cooking, housekeeping.
Who can assist the patient with ADLs?	Nurses, UAP's, PT, OT
What are Institutional ADLs?	Activities a person performs that interact with the world outside the house.
What are some examples of institutional ADLs?	Banking, church, volunteering, shopping, health care visits.
Who assists the client to perform these ADLs?	These ADLs are addressed by the Social Worker.
What implications does this have for interdisciplinary teams?	If the patient has basic ADL needs, they need a home health aide. IF they have institutional ADL needs then a Social Worker must be on the case.

AMPUTATION

What does AKA mean?	Above the knee amputation
What does BKA mean?	Below the knee amputation
To prevent post-op swelling, the stump should be ____ for ____ to ____ hours.	Elevated, 12 to 24 hours
AFTER THE FIRST 24 HRS (REMEMBER THE STUMP SHOULD BE ELEVATED DURING THIS TIME): If the patient had an AKA they should lie ____ several times per day.	Prone – to prevent flexion contracture
The #1 contracture problem in AKA is ____ of the ____.	Flexion of the hip

What will prevent hip flexion contracture after AKA?	Lying prone several times a day
What is the #1 contracture problem after BKA?	Flexion of the knee
How do you prevent flexion contracture of the knee after BKA?	Remind the patient to straighten their knee constantly while standing.
How often should a stump be washed?	Daily
When a stump is wrapped, the bandage should be tightest _____ and loosest _____.	Distally, proximally
If after a right BKA, the client c/o pain in his right toe, he is experiencing _____.	Phantom limb sensation
Phantom limb sensation is normal (T/F)	TRUE
Will phantom limb sensation subside?	In a few months
Is it acceptable for the patient to push the stump against a wall?	Yes, this is one way to toughen a stump so it will not break down due to the wear of the prosthetic leg; hitting it with pillows is another good method.

BASIC NUTRITION

Name the five/six essential nutrients	Carbohydrates, fats, proteins, vitamins, minerals, water
The major source of energy for the body is _____.	Carbohydrates
Carbohydrates provide _____ kcals per 1 gram.	Four
Sucrose is a sugar found in _____ and _____.	Fruits and vegetables
Is glycogen eaten in foods?	NO! It is a stored form of glucose. manufactured by the liver.

What is glycogen?	A stored form of glucose/energy
Lactose is a sugar found in _____.	Milk
What are the top three nutrients in Milk? When the body does not receive enough carbohydrates, it burns _____ and _____.	Lactose, Protein, Vitamin D (added) Protein and fats
The most concentrated source of energy for the body is _____.	Fats
Fats provide _____ kcals per 1 gram.	Nine
Fats carry vitamins __, __, __, and __.	A, D, E, K
The nutrient needed most for growth and repair of tissues is _____.	Protein (second best – vitamin C)
Proteins provide _____ kcals per 1 gram.	Four
Vitamins and minerals provide energy for the body. (T/F)	False – they are necessary for a body's chemical reactions.
Water is present in all body tissues. (T/F)	True (even bone)
Water accounts for ___ to ___% of an adult's total weight.	50 to 60%
Name the four basic food groups.	Milk & Cheese; Meat & Legumes; Vegetables & Fruits; Bread & Cereal
Water accounts for ___ to ___% of an infant's total weight.	70 to 75%
What is the most common measure of overweight and obesity?	BMI (body mass index in KG)
What BMI is considered underweight?	Less than 18.5

What BMI is considered overweight?	25 to 29.9
What BMI is considered obese?	30 and over
How do you describe a person with a BMI over 40?	MORBIDLY obese
What organ regulates appetite?	The hypothalamus
What are the top two complications of obesity?	Cardiovascular disease and Diabetes Mellitus.

BATHING AN INFANT

What solution and material are used to cleanse the eyes of an infant?	Plain water, cotton balls, washcloths
Can you use cotton swabs to clean the eyes, nares, or ears of an infant?	No, this is dangerous
Can you use the same cotton ball/washcloth edge for both eyes?	No, it would cross contaminate
Should you cover an unhealed umbilical site with the diaper?	No, fold the diaper down
What temperature is appropriate for the water used to bathe an infant?	100° to 105° F
What is the #1 purpose of a tepid sponge bath?	Lower body temperature during fever.
How should the temperature of the water be tested if no thermometer is available?	Dropping water on inside surface of your forearm.
With which body part do you begin when bathing an infant?	Eyes, always

When cleansing an infant's eye, cleanse from outer to inner canthus?	No, inner to outer.
Should you retract the foreskin of a 5- week-old male, uncircumcised infant to cleanse the area?	No, not until foreskin retracts naturally and without resistance – then it should be retracted, cleansed, and replaced.
When sponge-bathing with tepid water the correct temp is _____.	98.6° F
How many days does it take for the umbilical stump to fall off?	7 to 14
The primary reason why an infant is draped during the bath is to provide privacy. (T/F)	False, the primary purpose of draping is to prevent chilling.
You may use friction to remove vernix caseosa from an infant's skin. (T/F)	False, it causes damage/bruising.
What solution is commonly used for care of the umbilical cord?	70% alcohol to promote drying (trend is toward soap and water)

BLADDER, EYE, AND EAR IRRIGATIONS

What is the purpose of an intermittent bladder irrigation through a Foley catheter?	To flush mucus out and keep the drainage catheter open and patent. (For information on Continuous bladder irrigation see Chapter 8 under BPH and prostatectomy.)
How often is a bladder irrigation performed?	Once a day (maybe twice if a lot of mucus).
What solution is used for a bladder irrigation?	Normal saline (0.9 NaCl) ONLY.
Does a bladder irrigation need to be performed with sterile technique?	In the hospital, Yes. In the home, No.
What do you use to do a bladder irrigation?	A 60 mL syringe with a Toomey tip.
What is the purpose of an eye irrigation?	To clean mucus or foreign material from the eye or administer medications.

What should you clean before an eye irrigation?	The lids and brows and lashes of the patient should be cleaned with moist cotton balls. Use a NEW cotton ball with each stroke.
How do you wipe an eye correctly?	From inner canthus n(corner) to outer canthus (corner).
Direct the flow of the irrigant into what part of the eye?	In the conjunctival sac from inner to outer.
How far away from the eye should you hold the irrigating syringe?	About an inch.
What do you irrigate the eye with?	0.9 NaCl (Normal saline).
Why is an ear irrigation performed?	To remove wax or foreign material from the ear.
Before an ear irrigation is performed to remove WAX what needs to be done?	The patient needs wax softening ear drops for several days before the irrigation.
Are eye and ear irrigations done with sterile solutions?	Yes. Both with sterile Normal saline at room temperature.

CASTS AND TRACTION

What part of your hand do you use to handle a wet cast?	The Palm
Upon what do you support a cast while it dries?	Pillows (no plastic covers)
How long does it take a cast to dry?	24 hours
Should you cover a wet cast?	No
Should you use a heat lamp or hair dryer or fan to help dry a cast?	NO- heat lamp and hair dryer **YES-fan**
What signs or symptoms would you report if they were present after the cast application?	Numbness, tingling, burning, pallor, unequal or absent pulses, unequal coolness.
If there is inflammation under a cast, it will be evident in a _____ spot.	"Hot"

To prevent irritation of the skin near the edges of a cast the edges should be _____.	Petaled
What type of cast causes cast syndrome?	A body cast
What causes cast syndrome?	Anxiety and stress leading to sympathoadrenal shutdown of the bowel.
What is the #1 symptom of cast syndrome?	Nausea and vomiting due to bowel obstruction
What is the #1 treatment of cast syndrome?	NPO, and NG tube for decompression
A dry cast is (gray or white)	White
Is a dry cast (dull or shiny).	Shiny
A dry cast is (dull or resonant) to percussion.	Resonant
Traction is used to _____ a fracture, relieve _____ _____ and prevent de-_____.	Reduce and immobilize; muscle spasm; deformities
Can skin traction be removed for skin care?	Yes
Can the client be removed from skeletal traction?	No
Name 3 types of skin traction.	Bucks, Bryants, Pelvic
Name 3 types of skeletal traction	Cranial tongs, Thomas splints with Pearson attachments, 90° to 90°
What type of traction is most used for hip fracture in adults?	Bucks
What type of traction is most used for hip fracture in children?	Bryants
In what position should the bed be if the patient is in pelvic traction?	Semi-fowlers with knee bent
To ensure that Bryant's traction is working the child's hip/sacrum should be _____.	Off the bed enough to slip a hand between the sacrum and the bed.

What is the advantage of balanced countertraction?	You can easily move the patient around in bed.
Patients in Russell's traction are particularly prone to _____.	Thrombophlebitis
When a patient is in a Buck's traction they may turn to the _____ side.	Unaffected

CELIAC AND LOW GLUTEN DIET

Celiac's disease is a _____ disease.	Malabsorption
The client with celiac's cannot tolerate _____.	Gluten
Gluten is a _____.	Protein
What does gluten do to the intestines of the client with celiac's disease?	It destroys the lining of the intestine
The stools of a client with celiac's disease are _____, _____, and _____ _____.	Large, greasy, foul-smelling
Clients with celiac's disease do not absorb what mineral?	Iron
Clients with celiac's disease don't absorb fats; therefore, they don't absorb ____ ____ ____.	Fat soluble vitamins
What are the four fat-soluble vitamins?	A, D, E, K
Malabsorption of which vitamin leads to bleeding disorder?	Vitamin K, remember do not mix up potassium with vitamin K
What will the abdomen of clients with celiac's disease look like?	Distended with flatus
What is the #1 treatment of celiac's disease?	Gluten-free diet
Vegetables are allowed or not allowed?	Allowed
Fruits are allowed or not allowed?	Allowed

Grains of all kinds are prohibited. (T/F)	FALSE
What grains are allowed in a gluten-free diet?	Rice and corn
What grains are not allowed in a gluten-free diet?	Wheat, oats, rye, alfalfa, barley
Are foods made with wheat, oat or rye flour allowed?	No
Is milk allowed on a gluten-free diet?	Yes
Are meats allowed on a gluten-free diet?	Yes, but watch for breaded meats and hot dogs/lunch meats-may have grain in them and are not allowed.
Are eggs allowed on a gluten-free diet?	Yes
Is commercial ice cream allowed on a gluten-free diet?	No, even though it is a milk product, commercial ice cream has grain in it.
Are puddings allowed on a gluten-free diet?	No, for the same reason ice cream isn't
Which soups are not allowed on a gluten-free diet?	Creamed soups-these often have flour.

CHOLESTEROL IN THE DIET

The meats that are highest in cholesterol are _____ meats.	Organ meats, liver, heart, brains, kidneys
The meats that are second highest in cholesterol are the _____.	Shell seafood (shrimp, crab, lobster)
Egg white is (high/low) in cholesterol?	Low
Egg yolk is (high/low) in cholesterol?	High
The three meats lowest in cholesterol are _____, _____ and _____.	Chicken, pork, mutton
Milk is (high/low) in cholesterol.	Low
Is cheese high in cholesterol?	Only moderate, not really that high

Which oils are high in cholesterol?	Animal oils
Is cholesterol a triglyceride?	No
Do plant foods contain any cholesterol?	No, not many

FIBER IN THE DIET

Increasing dietary fiber intake lowers the risk of _____ of the _____.	Cancer, colon
Foods lose some or all of their fiber when they are _____, _____, _____, or _____.	Processed, cooked, peeled, refined
Whole grains and grain products are (high/low) in fiber.	High
Fruits are (high/low) in fiber.	High
Vegetables are (high/low) in fiber.	High
Milk and milk products are (high/low) in fiber.	Low
Meats are (high/low) in fiber.	Low
Nuts, seeds, and legumes are (high/low) in fiber.	Low
Which has the highest fiber? Grains, fruits, Vegetables, nuts.	Grains, especially bran
When a person increases fiber in the diet they should do so _____.	Slowly
Side effects of a high fiber diet include _____ and the malabsorption of _____.	Gas (flatus), minerals
Of milled bread, enriched bread, fortified bread & whole grain bread; which is highest in fiber?	Whole grain

HYGIENE

Which types of clients should have their toenails trimmed only by an HCP?	Diabetics, peripheral vascular disease, very thick nails.
Two purposes of bed bath are...	Cleanse the skin, provide comfort
The typical hospital client (should/should not) wear their dentures.	Should
What type of movement should be used for cleansing eyes?	Inner to outer canthus
Before applying elastic hose, the nurse should...	Elevate the client's legs for 3 to 5 minutes to decrease venous stasis
Clients on what class of drugs should use an electric razor?	Anticoagulants (heparin/coumadin/lovenox)
When a client is unable to hold his dentures firmly in his mouth, the nurse should...	Leave them out
How often should mouth care be performed for those clients on oxygen?	Every 2 hours
Should linens be shaken or patted into place during bed making? Why or why not?	No, both shaking and patting spread microorganisms.
How often should mouth care be given to mouth breathers?	Every 2 hours
Should lemon and glycerin swabs be used to cleanse the mouth?	No, they are not cleansing agents. They are used AFTER cleansing as a moistening agent.
How should a client's toenails be trimmed?	Straight across
Are nurses permitted to give perineal care to clients of the opposite sex?	Yes
Clients on what type of therapy must use a safety blade razor (non-electric)?	Oxygen therapy; since an electric razor could cause sparks.

How should a nurse carry soiled linen?	In a neat bundle held away from the body.
When giving a bed bath, on which body part should the nurse begin work?	The eyes
Give three reasons for giving a back rub.	Comfort, stimulate circulation, relaxation, stimulate muscles....
The greatest danger in placing water in the mouth of the unconscious patient during oral hygiene is...	Aspiration
When shaving a client, water used should be more (hot/cold) than bath water?	Hot
What does evening or hour of sleep (hs) care consist of?	Oral hygiene, washing face/hands, back rub, and tightening linens.
What is a dentifrice?	Agents which promote adherence of dentures to gums, i.e., Polygrip.
What is sordes?	Crusts on the tongue and gums due to improper oral hygiene.
What action will facilitate the trimming of brittle toenails?	Soaking in warm water.
Should the client roll the elastic stocking down to wash legs? Why or why not?	No, it can cause a constricting band about the ankle/foot.
Elastic stockings should be removed for the bath. (T/F)	TRUE
When should a patient put on TED hose?	Before getting out of bed (before the swelling occurs).

INTAKE AND OUTPUT

What fluids count as fluid intake?	Any food that turns to liquid if left at room temperature.

How is ice counted in intake?	Ice is counted by recording half the volume. So 30 mL of ice is 15 mL of intake.
Is pudding counted in intake.	Yes, it turns liquid at room temperature.
Is ice cream counted as intake?	Yes, it turns liquid at room temperature.
Is jello counted as intake?	Yes, it turns liquid at room temperature.
If the question includes 6 ounces of steak is that included on the intake?	NO, Meat is solid at room temperature. Just because a food is measured in ounces does not make it liquid.
Do you have to include the volume of liquid medications in the Intake record?	Yes, and then water given to have them swallow the medication.
What is the lowest acceptable rate of hourly urine output?	The client should void at least 30 mL per hour for an adult.
What is the minimum hourly urine output of urine for an infant?	1 mL per Kilogram per hour. So a baby weighs 3 kilograms the output should be 3 mL per hour.
How much does a liter of urine weigh?	1 kilogram (2.2 lbs)
If a patient retains 1500 mL of fluid how much weight will they gain?	1.5 kilogram. Remember 1000mL = 1 kilogram.
What should the adult 24-hour fluid intake be?	2500-3000 mL.
Should the nurse include IV piggybacks in the Intake?	Yes
Should the nurse include fluid collected in all drains and tubes in the output?	Yes
Does output JUST include urine?	No, it includes ANY fluids from the body that can be measured.
What is a good way to measure urine output for an incontinent infant?	Weigh the diapers. Remember 1000 mL = 1 Kilogram.

LIFE-CYCLE NUTRITION

By the end of the first six months of life an infant's birthweight should _____.	Double
By the end of the first year of life an infant's birthweight should _____.	Triple
The ideal food for infants is _____.	Breast milk
Breast milk contains substances that increase immunities. (T/F)	TRUE
Bottle-fed infants do not bond well with their mothers. (T/F)	FALSE
The one nutrient that commercial formulas are typically low in is _____.	Iron
Breast milk does not contain iron. (T/F)	False, however, it does not contain enough iron- so they should be fed iron fortified cereal starting at 6 months.
At what age should the infant be fed cows/goats milk?	Not before 12 months.
What is the major problem with feeding an infant skim milk?	They don't get enough calories and don't grow. Dehydration from excessive solute load and inability to concentrate urine.
When should the infant be introduced to textured solid food? (What age?)	4 to 6 months
What is the first food that an infant should be introduced to?	Iron fortified rice cereal
When forced to eat, the preschool child will....	Rebel
Parents of preschool children should be taught that as long as the child eats _____ good nutritious meal(s) per day, they should not make eating food an issue.	One
Refusal to eat is common in preschoolers. (T/F)	True, but still offer a variety.

Youngsters develop food preferences by...	Observing significant people in their environment.
School-age children grow at a slower rate than infants, toddlers or adolescents. (T/F)	TRUE
What dietary strategy is most appropriate for the industrious school-age child?	Wholesome snacks because they are often too busy to eat.
Girls in adolescence need more calories than adolescent boys. (T/F)	False, boys need more calories.
Adolescents should take vitamin supplements. (T/F)	TRUE

Na^+ (SODIUM) IN FOOD

Vegetables highest in Na^+ are _____.	Canned vegetables
The fruit food that is highest in Na^+ is _____.	Tomato sauce
As a rule, fresh meats are _____ in Na^+.	Low
As a rule, canned meats are _____ in Na^+.	Very high
As a rule, smoked foods are _____ in Na^+.	Very high
As a rule, fruits are _____ in Na^+.	Low
As a rule, vegetables are _____ in Na^+.	Low
As a rule, which are higher in sodium.... vegetables or fruits?	Vegetables
As a rule, which are higher in sugars...vegetables or fruits?	Fruits
As a rule, breads/cereals are _____ in Na^+.	Moderately high

As a rule, processed meats and cheeses are _____ in Na$^+$.	Very high
Margarine is much lower in Na$^+$ than butter. (T/F)	False, it is the same.
As a rule, breads/cereals are _____ in Na$^+$.	Moderately high
Salt substitutes contain potassium (T/F).	True, so beware.

NASOGASTRIC TUBE

An NG tube is inserted into the _____ via the _____.	Stomach, nares
You can feed a client through a NG tube (T/F)	TRUE
When an NG tube is being used for decompression what is happening?	The stomach is being emptied of its contents by suction.
NG tubes are used to pump the stomach of drug overdose clients. (T/F)	TRUE
What does gavage mean?	Feed a client with a tube.
What does lavage mean?	To continuously irrigate the stomach via a NG.
When an NG tube is used to stop gastric hemorrhage, it is irrigated with _____ _____.	Iced tap water
How long do you irrigate an NG with iced tap water when the stomach is bleeding?	Until the irrigating solution comes back out clear.
What is the maximum suction level used to decompress the GI tract via a NG?	25 mm Hg
Why are Salem sump tubes best suited for safe gastric suctioning?	Because they have vents that prevent damage to the gastric mucosa.
When an NG tube is in for a long time it must be replaced every _____ to _____ weeks.	2 to 3

People with a NG tube will breathe through their _____.	Mouth (mouth care is important)
The best way that the nurse can check if the NG is in the stomach is	1. Measure external length of the tube 2. Test pH of gastric contents 3. Auscultate gastric air bubble **IN THAT ORDER**
Before you put anything down the NG you must do what?	You must check to see if the NG placement is in the stomach.
In what position should the client be when a NG is being inserted?	Sitting up with the head slightly extended until the tube reaches the back of the throat then have them mildly flex the neck to push the tube in all the way.
How do you determine how far to put a NG tube in?	Measure from the tip of the nose to the back of the ear then to the xiphoid process.
In what position should the client be during a continuous NG tube feeding?	Head of the bed must be elevated 30 degrees (semi-fowler's would be acceptable).
What should you do after removing the NG tube?	Oral hygiene, then a drink of water

PATIENT CONTROLLED ANALGESIA--PCA PUMP

The client on a PCA pump is less likely to have post-operative complications than the client without a PCA pump. (T/F?)	True, because the comfortable patient moves around more and is less likely to get thrombo-phlebitis, pulmonary embolus, fatigue, ileus, and pneumonia.
Clients with COPD are not good candidates for PCA pumps. (T/F?)	True, due to the effects of narcotics on central respiratory control.
Name the three most common uses of PCA techniques.	Post-operative pain, cancer pain, sickle-cell crisis pain.
PCA pumps allow a more constant level of serum drug than conventional analgesia. (T/F?)	TRUE
A major disadvantage of PCA pumps is that the client can take too much medication. (T/F?)	False, it is not possible for the client to overdose due to the lock-out feature.

Clients on PCA pumps use more medication than those receiving IM injections. (T/F?)	False, they use less.
A disadvantage of PCA pumps is that the client does not ambulate as early due to the machine. (T/F?)	False, PCA clients ambulate earlier, and they pull their machine with them.
When discontinuing a PCA infusion it is acceptable to discard the drug cartridge. (T/F?)	False, the whole cartridge system must be returned to the pharmacy due to federal narcotic control laws.

PATIENT POSITIONING

What is the supine position?	Patient lying on back with head only SLIGHTLY elevated. (Remember SuPINE is on the sPINE)
What is another name for supine?	Dorsal recumbent.
What is Fowler's position?	Patient on back with the head of the bed (HOB) elevated 45-60 degrees.
What degree elevation is LOW Fowler's?	15-30 degrees elevation of HOB
What degree elevation is Semi Fowler's?	30–45-degree elevation of HOB
What degree elevation is High Fowler's?	Almost sitting at 90 degrees.
What is orthopneic position?	Patient sitting leaning forward over a overbed table with their arms on the table.
What is another name for orthopneic position?	Tripod position.
What is prone position?	Patient lying flat on abdomen.
Where must you place pillows when pronating a patient?	Under head and neck, under abdomen, and under lower legs (but not feet).
What do you do with the client's head when pronating a patient?	Turn it to the side.
What is lateral position?	Lying on the side.

Which leg is more "in front of" the other in lateral position?	The top leg.
In what position are the hip and knee joints in lateral position?	They are flexed.
Where do you place pillows in lateral positioning?	Under the head, patient hugs a pillow and a pillow between their knees.
What is Sim's position?	The patient is halfway between prone and lateral. The upper knee is flexed, and the lower leg is almost extended.
What is Sim's used for?	Mostly for rectal procedures (enemas/colonoscopies.)
What is Lithotomy position?	Patient on their back with hips and knees flexed and thighs apart. (Feet may or may not be in stirrups)
What is lithotomy position primarily used for?	Vaginal examination and childbirth.
What is Trendelenburg's Position?	The patient flat with HOB down and foot if bed elevated. Arms are tucked at the sides.
For what is Trendelenburg used?	Postural drainage of upper lobes of lung. Old position for hypotensive crisis ...not the best today. Can be used for prolapsed cord.
In what position do you place an intubated and ventilated client with severe covid 19 infections of the lungs?	Prone for periods during the day and night.
In what position do you place MOST post-operative clients in PACU (recovery room)?	Lateral position.
In what position do you place MOST postoperative patients on the unit.	Semi-Fowler's OR on side with incision UP.

IN what positions do you place patients who had a pneumonectomy or a biopsy?	Side lying with the surgical site DOWN.
In what position do you place a client with cranial issues.	Low Fowler's (HOB up 15 degree).
In what position do you place a client with pelvic inflammatory disease?	Semi Fowler's or higher.
In what position would you place a client in respiratory distress?	Tripod or orthopneic position.

POSTMORTEM CARE

Immediately after a patient dies, in what position do you place their body?	Supine with head of bed slightly elevated.
Why this position?	Because "liver mortis" can occur quickly and discolor the face to a blue/purple.
If the patient is a donor what should the nurse do with the life support measures even after brain death is confirmed?	Keep the patient on full life support until harvesting of the organs is completed.
What should the nurse do with tubes and lines when a client is to undergo an autopsy.	If the client has died and will be undergoing an autopsy to establish cause of death (usually in criminal case) ALL lines and tubes remain in.
If the patient is NOT a donor and NOT an autopsy candidate, what should the nurse do with all lines, tubes and life support measures upon their death?	Remove all support measures, tubes, and lines, **except for IV lines**. Because Fluid losses from IV removal can affect mortuary care cap IV lines and let the mortician remove them.
If they fit should dentures be placed in the deceased patient's mouth after death?	YES, so the face does not lose shape for the mortuary care.
If the culture does not forbid it should the nurse take measures to close the mouth?	YES
If the culture allows it, should the nurse take measures to close the eyes?	YES

Should the nurse clean up the client after death.	YES
Should the nurse place an incontinence pad under the patients' buttocks?	YES
Should the nurse dress the patient in their pajamas?	NO, a clean gown.
After all these things are finished, can the family come to the bedside?	Yes, and allow them time.
After the family leaves is the gown removed?	YES, then a shroud is used. Follow instructions on the shroud kit... they are all different.
Who establishes and records time of death.	The HCP.
In how many places should the ID of the body be placed?	2, on the body per protocol and on the shroud.

TENS

What does TENS stand for?	Transcutaneous electrical nerve stimulator
Is it an invasive procedure?	No, the skin is never broken.
Can it be used for acute or chronic pain?	Both
TENS use is based upon the _____ _____ of pain relief.	Gate control
TENS electrodes stimulate (large/small) diameter fibers.	Large--this is the basis of the gate control theory.
TENS electrodes are placed onto the	Skin
Can TENS units be placed over an incision to decrease incisional pain?	Never
Patients with what other mechanic device in use cannot use TENS?	Cardiac pacemaker

How often should the patient be taught to change the TENS electrodes?	Every day
How is a dorsal-column stimulator different that a TENS unit?	Dorsal column stimulation electrodes are surgically implanted by the spinal cord; the patient must undergo a laminectomy to place the DCS electrodes.

WOUND CARE

For what reason are Montgomery straps used?	Permit you to remove and replace dressings without using tape (protects the skin).
Sutures in general are removed by the ___ day.	7th
Leaving a wound open to air decreases infection by eliminating what three environmental conditions?	Dark, warm, moist
To remove tape always pull (toward/away) from the wound.	Toward (this way you don't put pressure/pull on the suture line).
Define contusion.	Bruise(internal)
Define debridement.	Removal of necrotic tissue from a wound
What is the purpose of a wound drain?	Remove secretions from the area so healing occurs.
To prevent germs from getting into or out of a wound you should use what type of dressing?	An occlusive dressing
What solution is put onto the skin to protect it from the irritating effects of the tape?	Tincture of benzoin
With what is a wound closed in first intention?	Sutures or steri-strips, staples
What is another name for second intention?	Granulation
When swabbing an incision, you should start at the incision or 1 inch away from the incision?	Start at the incision and move outward.

After you remove soiled dressings and before you put on the sterile dressing you must....	Wash your hands and put on sterile gloves.
What is meant by the phrase "advance the drain 1 inch"?	You pull the drain out 1 inch.
After advancing a Penrose drain you (should/should not) cut off the excess drain?	Should
When a dressing is saturated, germs can enter the wound from the outside. (T/F)	True, by a process called capillary action.
When is a bad time to change dressings?	Mealtime
Define laceration.	Cut

CHAPTER 6

PHARMACOLOGY

BLOOD TRANSFUSION #1

What does a type and cross match indicate?	Whether the client's blood and donor's blood are compatible
What should the nurse measure before starting a transfusion?	The vital signs
With what solution should blood be transfused?	0.9 normal saline
How many nurses are required to check the blood?	2
What happens when blood is administered with Dextrose IVs?	The cells clump together and don't flow well
How long can unit of blood be on the unit before it must be started?	Less than ½ hour
If a transfusion reaction occurs what should the nurse do first?	Stop the blood flow, start running the saline
What should the nurse do with the IV line if transfusion reaction is suspected?	Keep it open with saline
What is urticaria?	Hives-a sign of a reaction
If a transfusion reaction is suspected, what two samples are collected and sent to the lab?	Urine and blood
If a unit of blood is infused through a central line it must be _____.	Warmed
Which of the following are signs of transfusion reaction? Bradycardia, fever, hives, wheezing, increased blood pressure, low back pain?	Low back pain, wheezing, fever, hives
What blood test must be done before a transfusion?	Type and cross match

BLOOD TRANSFUSION #2

What are the three types of transfusion reactions that can occur?	Hemolytic, Febrile, Allergic
What would you do first if you suspected a transfusion reaction?	STOP the blood and start the saline IV.
What are the signs and symptoms of a hemolytic transfusion reaction?	Shivering, HA, Low back pain, increased pulsed increase respirations, decrease blood pressure, Oliguria, Hematuria.
When is a hemolytic transfusion reaction likely to occur?	In the first 10-15 min.
What are the signs and symptoms of a Febrile transfusion?	All the symptoms of a hemolytic plus an increased temperature, confusion, and possibly coughing up blood (hemoptysis).
When is a febrile reaction likely to occur?	Within the first 30 min.
What are the signs and symptoms of an allergic transfusion reaction?	Very different than the other two: Urticaria, wheezing, pruritus (itching), join pain (arthralgia).
When does an allergic transfusion reaction occur?	Any time after the blood is started and even hours later.
What other things are appropriate to do after stopping the blood and starting the saline IV in a reaction?	Call Health care provider (HCP) get a blood sample, get a urine sample, monitor vitals. SEND THE UNIT OF BLOOD that causes the reaction to the lab.
What are three reasons for a blood transfusion?	Restore blood volume in hemorrhage, maintain HGB in anemia, replace specific blood components.
What does blood typing mean?	Checking for surface antigen on the RBC (A, B, AB, O)
What does cross matching mean?	Mixing a little of the client's blood with the donor blood and looking for agglutination (clumping).

When does typing and cross matching need to be done?	Whenever a client is to get a blood product. It is only good for 24 hours.
What blood test identifies Rh factor?	Coombs test
What is the difference between whole blood and packed RBC?	Packed RBCs don't have as much plasma or liquid volume as whole blood.
What would you do if the client has an increased temperature and was supposed to get blood?	Call the HCPbe cause blood is often held with an elevated temperature.
How long should it take for one unit of blood to infuse?	From 1 to 3 hours
How long should a RN stay with the patient after beginning and transfusion?	15 to 30 minutes
What blood type is the universal recipient?	AB
What blood type is the universal donor?	O
Can blood be given immediately after removal from refrigeration?	No, it must be allowed to warm for about 20 to 30 minutes (maximum).
What is the routine for vital sign measurement with a transfusion?	Once before administration and every 15 minutes X2 after started, then every hour until transfusion is completed.

CARE OF THE CLIENT WITH A CESIUM IMPLANT FOR CANCER OF THE CERVIX

What is the big danger to staff when caring for a client with cesium implant?	Radiation hazard
What are the three principles to protect yourself from radiation hazards?	Time, distance, shielding
Will the woman with a cesium implant have a Foley?	Yes
From where should the nurse provide care to the client with cesium implant?	The head of the bed

How can a woman with a cesium implant move in bed?	Only from side to side
What four symptoms should be reported to the physician?	Profuse vaginal discharge, elevated temp, nausea, vomiting (these indicate infection and perforation)
Should pregnant staff care for a client with a cesium implant?	No
Can the woman with a cesium implant have the HOB elevated?	Yes, only 45° maximum.
From where should the nurse talk to the client?	The entrance to the room.
Is bed rest necessary when a woman has a cesium implant in place?	Yes, absolute bed rest
What type of diet is this woman on?	Low residue
No nurse should attend the client more than _____ hours per day.	One half hour
What would you do if the implant comes out?	Pick it up with forceps only- never touch it with your hand even if you are wearing gloves.
Should the nurse provide perineal care for the client with an implant?	No, risk of radiation hazard

CENTRAL LINES

The #1 problem with central lines is _____.	Infection
How often should central line dressings be changed?	QOD-every other day
What type of dressing is applied to a central line insertion site?	Sterile occlusive
Can drugs be piggybacked into central-TPN?	No, use another lumen.

When changing central line tubing the patient should be told to _____.	Turn his head away from site, hold breath, and perform the Valsalva maneuver
If a central line is found accidently open the patient should be positioned on his ____ ____.	Left side

CHEMOTHERAPEUTIC AGENT TOXICITIES

Cytoxan cyclophosphamide	Hemorrhagic cystitis
Cisplatin	Peripheral neuropathy, constipation, ototoxicity
Bleomycin	Pulmonary fibrosis
Adriamycin	Cardiotoxicity
Vincristine	Peripheral neuropathy, constipation
DTIC--dome	Flu-like symptoms
Methotrexate	Toxic to just about every organ except to heart, toxicity made worse with aspirin.

Constipation = adynamic ileus due to neurotoxicity
Peripheral neuropathy = foot drop, numbness, and tingling (paresthesia), hoarseness, jaw pain, constipation

CONVERSIONS

1 kg = _____mL	1000
1 in = _____cm	2.5
1 tsp =_____mL	4 to 5
1 g = _____mg	1000
1 L = _____ mL	1000
1 oz = _____mL	30

1 kg = _____lb	2.2
1 tbs = _____mL	15
1 tbs = _____tsp	3

DRUG TOXICITIES

What visual experiences will patients with digitalis toxicity have?	Yellow/green halos around lights
The signs of lithium toxicity are _____ (muscle symptom), _____ (abdominal sign), and thirst.	Tremor, nausea, and vomiting
Lithium carbonate is given for _____ disorder.	Bipolar (manic-depressive)
When a patient is on lithium you must watch for a decrease in _____.	Sodium
Theophylline is a broncho-_____ used to treat _____.	Dilator, asthma
Digitalis toxicity exists when blood levels exceed _____.	2.0 ng/dl
The earliest sign of digitalis toxicity is ...	Nausea and vomiting with headache.
Is theophylline toxicity life-threatening?	Yes
Lithium toxicity occurs when blood levels are higher than _____ mEq/L.	2
The signs of theophylline toxicity are _____ (GI), _____ (heart), and _____ (muscle).	Nausea and vomiting (coffee ground emesis), tachycardia, tremors
What is the therapeutic blood level of theophylline?	10 to 20
Digitalis is a cardiac _____, used to _____ the contraction of cardiac muscle.	Glycoside, increase

Theophylline toxicity exists when the blood level is above _____.	20

EYE DRUGS #1

Carbonic Anhydrase inhibitors	Treat glaucoma, decreases aqueous humor production, diuresis, Diamox is an example.
Anticholinergic	Dilates pupil, causes photophobia, used preoperatively for cataract removal, don't use in glaucoma, Atropine is an example.
Miotic	Constricts pupil; Timoptic, Pilocarpine are examples.
Mydriatic	Neo-synephrine is an example, tachycardia, photophobia, dilates pupil, do not use in glaucoma.

EYE DRUGS #2

What do carbonic anhydrase inhibitors do to the eye?	Decrease production of aqueous humor and thus decrease intraocular pressure.
Name the most common side effect of carbonic anhydrase inhibitors.	Diuresis
Which two groups of these drugs cause photophobia?	Mydriatics--anticholinergics
Which of these classes of drugs causes contact dermatitis?	Miotics
What do mydriatics do for the eye?	Dilate the pupil (My "D"iriatic--"D" for dilate)
What do miotics do for the eye?	Constrict the pupil.
Name one mydriatic.	Neo synephrine or Atropine
What do anticholinergics do for the eye?	Dilate the pupil, cycloplegia, paralyzes accommodation
What is cycloplegia?	Paralysis of the iris/pupil.

Which two of these classes of drugs cause tachycardia?	Mydriatics, anticholinergics (sympathetic effects)
What is the most common use for anticholinergics in the eye?	To cause cycloplegia, dilation, allowing eye exams.
How should eye ointments be given?	Placed on the lower inner eyelid, then have the client close eyes.
Name two anticholinergics used in the eye.	Cyclogel, atropine
Name one carbonic anhydrase inhibitor.	Diamox
How should eye drops be given?	Place drops into the lower conjunctival sac.
How is the flow of eye irrigational fluid directed?	From inner canthus to outer canthus.
Name two miotics.	Pilocarpine, Timpotic (or any drug ending in --lol).

IV MAINTENANCE

What gloves should a nurse wear when inserting an IV catheter?	Clean gloves to prevent a body fluid exposure.
What should be used to cleanse the IV insertion site?	Povidone-iodine/NOT alcohol.
What are the best veins to use when inserting most IV catheters?	The large veins of the lower arms (prefer the non-dominant arm.
What are poor sites for IV catheter insertion.	The veins of the back of the hand. The veins of the leg. Not in the arm after breast surgery on that side. Not in a limb with thrombophlebitis. Not in an arm with a hemodialysis fistula or shunt.
What rate is a low flow rate just to keep a vein patent for an adult?	30-60 mL/hour.
What is a low therapeutic IV flow rate for an adult?	60-90 mL/hour.

What is a moderate therapeutic IV flow rate for an adult?	100-150 mL/hour.
What is a HIGH therapeutic flow rate for an adult?	175-250 mL/hour.
Can you run IV infusions at rates higher than 250 mL/hour?	Yes, only in emergency situations with HCP monitoring.
How often should IV tubing be changed?	Every 72 hours.
How often is piggyback tubing changed?	Every 24 hours.
Which IV solution is best for tissue rehydration?	D5W
Which solution is best for IV blood pressure support?	Normal saline (o.9NaCl) or Lactated Ringer's
What is IV infiltration?	It is when the IV catheter is dislodged from the vein into the subcutaneous tissue.
What does an infiltration look like.	It is swollen, hard, cool, pale with no blood return.
What is phlebitis?	It occurs when the catheter and/or the medication causes a local inflammation of the blood vessel linings.
What does phlebitis look like?	The vein is erythematous (red), warm, painful, swollen with a possible red streak.
What should a nurse do if phlebitis or infiltration is suspected?	Discontinue the IV site and start any new site in a different extremity if possible.

MEDICATION ADMINISTRATION

Which is the best method for identifying clients accurately?	By ID name-band and patient verbal confirmation.
An emulsion is a mixture of _____ and _____.	Oil and H2O

Syrups and elixirs are of particular concern to diabetic clients because...	They contain sugars.
Oral medications have a (faster/slower) onset of action than IM drugs.	Slower
Oral medications have a (shorter/longer) duration of action than IM medications.	Longer
How should drugs that stain the teeth be administered?	By a straw.
A drug given by a parenteral route acts outside the GI tract. (T/F)	TRUE
Name the 4 most common parenteral routes of administrations.	SQ, IM, IV, ID (intradermal)
When blood is administered by IV the needle/ catheter should be _____ gauge.	18 gauge
You can administer up to _____ mL of a drug per site by IM injection in adults.	3 mL
Children should receive no more than _____ mL per site by IM injection.	2 mL
The preferred IM injection site for children under 3 is the _____ _____.	Vastus lateralis
Why is the dorsogluteal site not recommended for IM injection in children less than 3 years of age?	Because the muscle is not well developed yet.
Can 3 mL of fluid be administered per IM into the deltoid of an adult?	No, maximum of 1 mL.
The #1 danger when using the dorsogluteal site for IM injection is...	Damage to the sciatic nerve.
The preferred angle of injection to be used for IM administration is _____.	90°

The preferred length of needle to administer an IM injection is...	1 to 2 inches
The preferred gauge of needle for IM injection is....	21 to 22 gauge
Which type of medications are given by Ztrack injection?	Irritating, staining
How long is the needle kept inserted during Z-track injection?	10 seconds
What must be done to the equipment before injecting by Z-track method?	Change the needle
When giving a Z-track injection, the overlying skin is pulled (up/down/medially/laterally)	Laterally
Subcutaneous injection must be given at 45°. (T/F)	True (for boards), false--whatever angle gets it SQ without going IM. Insulin is given at 90 since the needle is shorter.
The preferred gauge of needle for injection for SQ injection is _____.	25 gauge
The preferred length of needle for SQ injection is _____.	5/8 inch
The intradermal route is primarily used for _____ _____.	Skin testing
Name the two sites used for intradermal injection.	Inner forearm, upper back
In general, the nurse should wear gloves when applying skin preparations such as lotions. (T/F)	TRUE
After using nose drops, the client should remain _____ for _____ minutes.	Supine, 5
Strict aseptic techniques are required when administering a vaginal medication. (T/F)	False, only "clean" technique or medical asepsis is necessary.

Before administering vaginal medications, the client is more comfortable if you ask them to _____.	Void
After administration of a vaginal drug the client should remain _____ for _____ minutes.	Supine, 10
Rectal suppositories with an oil base should be kept refrigerated. (T/F)	TRUE
Strict sterile technique is required when administering a drug per rectum. (T/F)	False, clean or medical asepsis.
The best way to ensure effectiveness of a rectal suppository is to...	Push the suppository against the wall of the rectum.
A rectal suppository is inserted _____ inches in an adult and _____ inches in a child.	4, 2
The client should remain supine for 5 minutes after having received a rectal suppository. (T/F)	False, they should be lying on their side for 5 minutes, not supine.
A suppository given rectally must be lubricated with a water-soluble lubricant. (T/F)	True, lubricate fingers also.
Eye medications can be given directly over the cornea. (T/F)	False, into the conjunctival sac, never the cornea; hold the dropper 1/2 inch above the sac.
Eye drops should be placed directly into the _____ _____.	Conjunctival sac
To prevent eye medication from getting into the systemic circulation you apply pressure to the _____ for _____ seconds.	Nasolacrimal sac, 10 (Press between the inner canthus and the bridge of the nose.)
The eye should be irrigated so that the solution flows from outer to inner canthus. (T/F)	False, it must flow from inner to outer (alphabetical: I®O)
If ear medications are not given at room temperature the client may experience...	Dizziness, nausea
To straighten the ear canal in the adult the nurse should pull the pinna _____ and _____.	Up, back

To straighten the ear canal in the young child under 3 the pinna should be pulled ___ and ____.	Down, back
After receiving ear drops the client should remain in _____ position for _____ minutes.	Side lying, 5
How far above the ear canal should you hold the dropper while administering ear drops?	½ inch
Liquid doses of medications should be prepared at _____ level.	Eye
Liquid drugs should be poured out of the side (opposite of/the same as) the label.	Opposite
It is safe practice to administer drugs prepared by another nurse. (T/F)	FALSE
In order to leave drugs at the bedside, you must have a physician's order. (T/F)	TRUE
Young infants accept medication best when given with a _____.	Dropper
It is safe practice to re-cap needles after injection. (T/F)	False, NEVER re-cap.
What do you do if you get blood in the syringe upon aspiration?	Remove the syringe immediately and apply pressure; you must discard the syringe and re-draw medication in a new syringe.

MEDICATION RECONCILIATION AND DISPOSAL

What is medication reconciliation?	It is when the CURRENT list of medications for a client is compared to the list of medications ORDERED for that patient?
Why is medication reconciliation performed?	Medication lists can be very long and developed over the years. Errors can occur in transcription, filling prescriptions and administration of medications. Reconciliation catches these errors.

Who is responsible to perform a medication reconciliation?	Traditionally, the HCP or prescribers. But more recently Pharmacists have been given this role in most states.
Do nurses do medication reconciliation?	NO, but they are responsible to be evaluating records for inconsistencies and recommending it.
What is the proper way to dispose of medication in the institution?	Return it to the Pharmacy.
Should a nurse send unused medications home with the family?	NO
What should the nurse do with unused liquid medication in a vial of injectable medication?	It can be disposed of by placing in a "sharps" box.
How should a nurse dispose of controlled substances?	If a portion of a controlled substance is to be "wasted", two nurses must witness the wasting.
How should patients in the community dispose of controlled substances?	They should turn them in to a local governmental "turn in" office. Do not lend or sell, or flush, or trash these medications.
Can a patient put non controlled medications in the trash?	Yes, if they are placed in plastic containers, the local refuse removal company will have guidelines.
Can a nurse get into legal trouble for having expired controlled substances in their home?	Yes

MEDICATIONS AND MEALTIME

Tagamet	Give with meals, remember Zantac does not have to be given with meals.
Capoten	Give on empty stomach, one hour before meals (antihypertensive).
Apresoline	Given with meals (anti-hypertensive).
Iron with nausea	Give with meals.

Sulfonamides	Take with lots of water regardless of whether you give it at mealtime or not--Bactrim, Septra, Gantricin, i.e., used to treat UTI.
Codeine	Take with lots of water regardless of meals-to prevent constipation.
Antacids	Give on empty stomach 1 hr ac and hs.
Ipecac	Give with 200-300 mL water--not related to mealtime--this is an emetic (to make you vomit after ingestion of poisons--don't give if the poisons were caustic, or petroleum based).
Rifampin	Give on empty stomach (anti tuberculosis) remember Rifampin causes red urine.
Non-steroidal anti-inflammatory drugs	Give with food (for arthritis)
Aldactone	Give with meals (K--sparing diuretic).
Iron without nausea	Give on empty stomach with orange juice to increase absorption.
Penicillin	Give on empty stomach.
Erythromycin	Give on empty stomach (antibiotic).
Stool softeners	Take with lots of water regardless of mealtime.
Griseofulvin	Give with meals--especially high fat meals (anti-fungal).
Tetracycline	Do not give with milk products, do not give to pregnant women or children before age 8 or damage to tooth enamel occurs.
Theophylline derivative	Give with meals, ie, Aminophylline, Theodur-- (anti-asthmatic bronchodilator).

Steroids	Give with meals--remember taper the patient off these drugs slowly.
Pancreas pancreatin isozyme	Give with meals--these are oral enzymes used with children with cystic fibrosis to increase the absorption of the food they eat.
Para-amino salicylate sodium (PAS)	Give with meals/food--anti tuberculosis.
Colchicine	Give with meals --anti gout, remember if diarrhea develops, stop the drug.
Thorazine	Take with lots of water regardless of meals to prevent constipation. All drugs that end in "-zine" are major tranquilizers that also cause Pseudo Parkinson's or extra-pyramidal effects.
Carafate and sulcrafate	Give on empty stomach 1 hour before meals and at bedtime--remember these coat the GI tract and interfere with the absorption of other medications (give them by themselves).
Allopurinol	Give with meals and give with lots of water-anti-uric acid--used to treat gout and the purine build up seen in chemotherapy for cancer.

OXYGEN THERAPY

In addition to the nares, where else should the nurse assess for skin irritation when nasal cannulae are in use?	Behind and on top of the ears.
What are the two early signs of hypoxia?	Restlessness, tachycardia
What is the highest flow rate appropriate for nasal cannulae?	6 L/min
How often should the nares of a client with O2 by nasal cannulae be assessed for skin breakdown?	Every 6-8 hours

What is the maximal O2 flow rate for the client with COPD?	2 L/min
What are the signs of O2 toxicity?	Confusion, headache
What can happen if the client with COPD is given a high flow rate of O2?	They may stop breathing.
What is the problem with giving high flow rates of O2 by nasal cannulae?	Dries the mucous membranes.
Can a client smoke in the room when the O2 is turned off?	No, the O2 delivery device must be removed from the wall or the tank out of the room before a client can smoke.
When O2 is administered, it must be...	Humidified
Masks deliver higher or lower concentrations of O2 than nasal cannulae?	Higher
How often should the nurse check the flow rate of the O2?	At least once per shift
O2 is an explosive. (T/F?)	False, it does not explode--it supports combustion.

RADIATION THERAPY

What is the #1 difference between sealed and unsealed radiation?	Both are internal forms of radiotherapy; however, in sealed a solid object is placed in a body cavity. In unsealed a radioactive substance is injected in liquid form into a vein.
What are the three principles the nurse uses to protect self when caring for a client with a sealed radioactive implant?	Time, distance, shielding
What is another name for external radiation therapy?	Beam or X-rays

What is the difference between external radiation treatment and internal radiation treatment?	In external the tumor is bombarded with xrays, and nothing is placed in the body; in internal there is some radioactive substance introduced into the body.
Of sealed internal, unsealed internal, and external radiation treatment, which is MOST dangerous for the nurse?	Sealed internal then unsealed internal, external radiation treatment is of no danger to the nurse unless the nurse is in the radiation treatment room during the treatment.
Should pregnant nurses care for a patient receiving sealed internal radiotherapy?	Never. (Lawsuit time!)
Should pregnant nurses provide care for a patient receiving unsealed internal radiotherapy?	Maybe, as long as they don't contact body secretions.
What skin products should the patient receiving external radiotherapy AVOID?	No, ointments with metals like zinc oxide, no talcum powder.
Describe the hygiene measures that you teach the patient receiving external radiotherapy?	Use plain water only, no soaps, pat dry, can use cornstarch for itch.
What are the major side effects of radiotherapy?	Pruritis, erythema, burning, sloughing of skin, anorexia, nausea and vomiting, diarrhea, bone marrow depression
When the patient is receiving radioactive iodine, what precautions is/are most important?	Wear gloves while in possible contact with urine, special precautions taken to dispose of the urine.

TITRATION OF MEDICATIONS

What does "titration "mean?	It means that the HCP has not ordered a set flow rate for IV medications. The nurse calculates and adjusts the flow rate (usually hourly) based on a formula the HCP prescribes that includes critical parameters.

What are some parameters used to titrate a medication?	Blood pressure, pulse, respiratory rate, oxygen saturation, urine output. Laboratory values, weight, hemodynamic pressures, reflex irritability, LOC.
When a patient is having a medication titrated, must they have a IV pump?	YES
What is the most common frequency at which IV flow rates are changed in titration?	Hourly
Can Iv rates be increased during titration?	YES
Can IV rates be decreased during titration?	YES
Is the nurse ethically and legally responsible to accurately and timely administer drug titrations?	YES
What is a common name for titrations?	"Drips"
If the HCP orders an Insulin drip does the nurse have to start another IV site/line or can it be "piggybacked"?	An insulin drip cannot be piggybacked, and a new IV site/line must be established (unless the patient has a multiple lumen IV catheter.)
What do you use to titrate and insulin drip?	Watch the blood glucose.
Dopamine is titrated and treats what disorder?	**HYPO**tension
What do you monitor to titrate Dopamine?	The BP and urine output.
What organ system is Dopamine harmful to?	The kidneys… do not use with CKD (chronic kidney disease).
Dobutamine is titrated and used for what disorders?	It strengthens the heart in heart failure, and it raises blood pressure.
Does Dobutamine harm the kidneys?	NO. **Pay attention**, one drug starts with "**Dop**" and the other with "**dobut**". **Remember the one with a U is good for the Urine.**
What do you monitor to titrate Dobutrex?	BP and urine output.

Labetalol can be titrated and is used for what problem?	**HYPER**tension
What do you monitor to titrate Labetalol?	Heart rate (watch for bradycardia) and BP
Midazolam (Versed) can be titrated and is used in what situation?	To induce anesthesia and treatment of severe seizure.
What do you monitor to titrate Midazolam?	The LOC.
Propofol is titrated and is used in what situation?	Used for sedation.
What do you monitor to titrate Propofol?	The BP and LOC.
What do you have to monitor for adverse effects of Propofol (Diprivan)	Triglycerides and body enzymes ...think any blood test that measures anything that ends in -ASE!!!
Nitroglycerin can be titrated and is used for what problems?	Used for CHF after an MI, and for Hypertension.

TOTAL PARENTERAL NUTRITION

Give another name for TPN.	Hyperalimentation
Hyperalimentation contains hypertonic _____, _____ acids, _____, _____, and _____.	Glucose, amino acids, water, minerals, vitamins
TPN can be safely given via a central IV line. (T/F)	Yes, this is the preferred route.
TPN can be safely infused via a peripheral IV line. (T/F)	It can, but only for a very short period-48 to 72 hours maximum.
If a TPN solution is running too slow and is two hours behind, you can increase the rate 20%. (T/F)	No, never ever speed up the rate.
If a TPN infusion runs in too fast, it creates a _____osmolar imbalance.	Hyperosmalar--because of all the solutes.
It is okay however to slow the rate down if the client leaves the unit. (T/F)	False, never slow the rate down-it could cause hypoglycemia.

Pharmacology

What tests must the nurse perform every 6 hours when a patient is on TPN?	#1 accu check, #2 urine glucose/acetone
IV lipid emulsions can be given either central or peripheral. (T/F)	TRUE
Be certain to shake a lipid emulsion before administration. (T/F)	False, never shake it, shaking damages the molecules.
Into which port of a peripheral IV line can a lipid infusion be piggybacked?	The port closest to the insertion catheter site. More recently, lipids are included in the hyperalimentation bag and there is no separate administration of the lipids.

CHAPTER 7
REDUCTION OF RISK POTENTIAL

BLADDER CATHETERIZATION

How often should the urinary drainage bag be emptied?	Every 8 hours
What is the most common problem due to catheterization?	Urinary tract infections (UTI)
What is the most common organism to cause UTI with catheterization?	E. coli
What is the most common route for organisms to enter the bladder when catheterization is used?	Up through the inside of the catheter in the days following catheterization
To prevent urinary tract infections the urine should be (acidified/alkalinized).	Acidified: acidic urine is bacteriostatic. This is done by eating an ACID-ASH diet.
Name some foods that make acid urine.	Cranberry juice, apple juice (avoid citrus juices – they make alkaline urine), breads and meats.
Name some food that make alkaline urine.	Fruits and vegetables (except for cranberry and apple juice), milk/dairy.
What is important about the level of the urinary drainage bag?	Never have the bag at a higher level than the bladder.
How is the catheter taped in a male client?	To the lateral thigh or abdomen
How is the catheter taped in a female client?	To the upper thigh
What urinary pH prevents UTI?	Acidity, low pH
Should the drainage bag ever touch the floor?	No
Is it okay to routinely irrigate indwelling catheters?	No
What agents are best for catheter care?	Soap and water
What is the most effective way to decrease UTI with catheters?	Keep the drainage system closed, do not disconnect junctions of tubing.
Give some signs of infection in a Foley catheter.	Cloudy urine, foul smelling urine, hematuria

Is urinary incontinence an indication for catheterization?	No
Give three appropriate indications for bladder catheterization	Urinary retention, to check for residual, to monitor hourly output.
What are the top 2 diagnoses for a client with a catheter? Which is #1?	#1 – potential for infection; potential impairment of urethral tissue integrity.

BLOOD PRESSURE

What is systole?	The maximal force of blood on artery walls
What is diastole?	The lowest force of blood on artery walls
Accurate blood pressure is obtained by using a cuff that has a width of _____ of the arm.	Two-thirds
Which artery is most commonly used to measure blood pressure?	Brachial
Can the thigh ever be used to obtain a blood pressure?	Yes, but this is rare
When pressure is auscultated the first sound is the _____ measurement.	Systolic
The change in the character of the sounds is known as the _____.	First diastolic sound
The cessation of sounds is known as the _____.	Second diastolic sound
When 2 values are given in a blood pressure the first is the _____ measurement.	Systolic
When 2 values are given in a blood pressure (ie, 120/80), the 80 stands for the change in sounds or cessation of sounds?	Cessation of sounds
What is the normal adult blood pressure?	120/80
Abnormally high blood pressure is called _____.	Hypertension

What is the pulse pressure?	The difference between the systolic and the diastolic blood pressure.
If you deflate a cuff TOO SLOWLY, the reading will be too high or low? Why?	High, venous congestion makes the arterial pressure higher (increases resistance).
If you use too narrow of a cuff the reading will be too high or low?	High
Vasoconstriction will _____ blood pressure.	Increase
Vasodilation will _____ blood pressure.	Decrease
Shock will _____ blood pressure.	Decrease the blood pressure
Shock will _____ the pulse pressure.	Narrow (decrease)
Increased intracranial pressure will _____ the pulse pressure.	Widen (increase)
If my blood pressure is 190/110, what is my pulse pressure?	80 mm Hg

BLOOD SPECIMENS

What is MOST important measure to do when collecting blood specimens?	Identify the patient correctly.
When collecting blood cultures what is the most important action to take after correct ID?	Proper disinfection of the skin.
What should be used to cleanse the skin before blood cultures are drawn?	Chlorhexadine or an alcohol containing skin prep for 2 minutes.
How long should the nurse wait after cleansing the skin to perform the venipuncture?	Until the skin dries.
What two actions during obtaining the blood sample will cause bad results?	Pulling too hard on the syringe when withdrawing blood from the vein and getting the blood from a line.

How soon should blood cultures be transported to the lab?	As soon as possible.
When a patient has multiple blood specimen vials to be drawn, which should be drawn FIRST, SECOND?	Draw blood cultures FIRST; Coagulation specimens SECOND.
What blood specimens need to be protected from light after being drawn?	Specimens for measuring Vitamins.
What PPE is recommended for blood draws?	Goggles, clean gloves, and something to cover clothing.
In what containers should blood specimens be transported?	In Biohazard marked bags/containers.

CONTACT LENSES AND HEARING AIDS

Should hearing aids be removed before going for surgery?	Yes, but just before surgery
Hearing aids are more useful in sensory or conductive hearing loss?	Conductive
Some women experience discomfort when wearing contact lenses during pregnancy or menstrual periods. (T/F)	TRUE
Should a client sleep with the hearing aid in place?	No
What are the two most-common causes of whistling and squealing of a hearing aid?	Loose ear mold, low battery
What solution should be used to clean a hearing aid?	Soap and water
What solution is best to use if you intend to remove a client's contact lenses?	Sterile saline
Hearing aids make sounds more distinct and clearer. (T/F)	False, they only amplify--make it louder, they do not clarify.

Can you use alcohol on the earmold of a hearing aid?	No, it dries and cracks it.
The connecting tube of a hearing aid can be cleansed with _____.	A pipe cleaner.
What is the most common complication of malpositioned lenses in the comatose or confused patient?	Corneal ulceration
In an emergency situation when hard contact lenses are unable to be removed, what should the nurse do?	Slide the lens entirely over the sclera--get it off the cornea.

CYSTOSCOPY

Define cystoscopy.	Direct visualization of the urethra and bladder through a cystoscope.
What would you do if the client has any one of the following after cystoscopy: bladder spasm, burning, frequency?	Record it but no need to call the HCP.
What would you do if the client's urine had red blood in it after cystoscopy?	Call the HCP.
What would you do if the client's urine was pink tinged after cystoscopy?	Record it in the notes, no need to call the HCP.
Is the client NPO before a cystoscopy?	No, not unless a child with a general anesthetic -- in fact with adults you should encourage fluids.
Are enemas required before cystoscopy?	No, but may be ordered.
Should you encourage fluids after cystoscopy?	Yes
Is a signed informed consent required for cystoscopy?	Yes
What vital sign changes are most ominous after cystoscopy?	A fall in the blood pressure and increase in the pulse--increasing hemorrhage.

Is the client sedated for a cystoscopy?	It is done under local anesthesia. General anesthesia may be used for a child.
What drug is most frequently given before cystoscopy?	Valium or Diazepam

ELECTROENCEPHALOGRAM (EEG)

What does an EEG measure?	Measures electrical activity generated by the brain.
When are there activity restrictions after an EEG?	ONLY when sedatives are used, and then it's only necessary to keep side rails up.
Should the client wash his hair before an EEG?	Yes
What would you tell a client who says "What if I get shocked during my EEG?"	That is impossible since the test measures electrical activity coming FROM him, never to him.
Does a client have to be NPO before an EEG?	No, they should never be NPO, it could cause hypoglycemia and alter the EEG results.
What instructions are MOST important to give a client during an EEG?	Try not to move.
What should the client do after an EEG?	Wash their hair.
Should sedatives be given before an EEG?	Only if ordered as a pre-test medication.
How much sleep should the client get the night before an EEG?	At least 4 to 5 hours--unless it is a sleep deprivation EEG.
Do you need a signed informed consent for an EEG?	No
Should caffeine be limited before an EEG?	Yes. It should be eliminated for 24 hours before the test.

ESOPHAGOGASTRODUODENOSCOPY (EGD)

Define EGD.	Insertion of a fiber optic scope to visualize the esophagus, stomach, and duodenum.
What can be done during an EGD besides visualization?	Remove polyps, take specimens, coagulate bleeding vessels
Can EGD be done on an uncooperative client?	No
Does the client need to have the side rails up after EGD?	Yes, until sedative effects of valium have worn off.
Can an EGD be done on clients with GI bleeding?	Yes
Is the client sedated before EGD?	Yes, with valium (diazepam) Or another sedative.
What pre-test activities must be performed before the EGD?	Remove dentures, eyeglasses, sign consent, NPO after midnight.
When can an EGD client begin to eat after the test?	When gag reflex returns (knocked out with xylocaine).
Is an EGD a fasting procedure?	Yes, after midnight.
What drug is given to anesthetize the pharynx?	Xylocaine (a local anesthetic)
What are the complications of EGD?	Perforation of gut, aspiration secondary to emesis, respiratory arrest (due to valium).
What two discomforts are common during an EGD?	Vomiting and gagging
What is the most dangerous complication of an EGD?	Secondary respiratory arrest (valium)
What is the most common complaint after an EGD?	Sore throat

HYSTERECTOMY

What is a hysterectomy?	It is surgical removal of the uterus.
How long must a woman wait before having intercourse after hysterectomy?	4 to 6 weeks
Is the woman likely to have a foley in after a hysterectomy?	Yes
Are enemas common before a hysterectomy?	Yes
What would you do if the client complains of flank pain (back pain) after hysterectomy?	Call the HCP, probably had a ureter tied off accidently in surgery.
What are 2 common psychological reactions to hysterectomy?	Grief, depression
What causes thrombophlebitis after hysterectomy?	Venous stasis in the abdomen (the woman was in the vaginal lithotomy position for hours).
What sign would indicate the presence of thrombophlebitis?	A hard, red swelling in the posterior calf.
Should you assess for Homan's sign?	No. Homan's sign is no longer recommended as a test for thrombophlebitis because it can cause a clot to embolize.
How long does the woman need to be off oral contraceptives before hysterectomy?	Oral contraceptives should be discontinued 3 to 4 weeks preoperatively.
How long should a woman wait before lifting heavy objects after a hysterectomy?	2 months
How long does a lady have to wait before driving after a hysterectomy?	3 to 4 weeks
If the client complains of abdominal gas after a hysterectomy, the best intervention is...	Ambulation
What are two major complications of a hysterectomy besides hemorrhage?	Thrombus and pulmonary embolus, Urinary retention.

What body position should be avoided after hysterectomy?	Knee flexion (because it increases the chance of thrombophlebitis).
When will bowel sounds return after a hysterectomy?	After 24 hours, but before 72 hours.

INCREASED INTRACRANIAL PRESSURE

Untreated increased intracranial pressure (ICP) can lead to brain _____ and _____.	Herniation, death
ICP increases whenever anything unusual occupies _____ in the cranium.	Space
The earliest sign of increased ICP is ...	Change in LOC (Level of Consciousness)
The pulse pressure _____ when ICP is increased.	Widens
Whenever there is increased ICP the _____ blood pressure rises.	Systolic
When there is increased ICP the _____ blood pressure remains the same.	Diastolic
Which pulse rate is most commonly associated with increased ICP?	Bradycardia
In increased ICP the temperature (rises/falls).	Rises
Describe the respiratory pattern seen in increased ICP.	First, central hyperventilation (very early on) and at the end Cheyne-Stokes.
When ICP is increased, the pupils FIRST show...	Unilateral dilation with sluggish reaction.
Eventually in increased ICP the pupils become _____ and _____.	Fixed and dilated
Will the client with increased ICP have a headache?	Yes

What type of vomiting is present in increased ICP?	Projectile
Why does hyperventilation "treat" increased ICP?	It reduces CO2, resulting in vasoconstriction. CO2 is a vasodilator in the brain, vasodilatation would occupy more space and thus increase ICP more.
When ICP increases the patient is more likely to have fluids (encouraged/restricted).	Restricted to decrease edema in the brain.
What is papilledema and how is it related to increased ICP?	It is edema of the optic disc; it is present when increased ICP pushes brain tissue through the optic foramen. (You see it with an ophthalmoscope)
What environmental changes are necessary when there is increased ICP?	Dark, calm, quiet environment
When there is increased ICP the nurse should first ____ the ____ of the bed to ____ degrees.	Position; head; 10-30°
After positioning the HOB, the nurse should then....	Call the doctor
What activities/action MUST be avoided in the client with increased ICP?	Sneezing, coughing (non-productive), straining at stool or doing anything which requires the Valsalva maneuver.
When a patient has increased ICP, the nurse should (hyper/hypo) ventilate the patient?	Hyperventilate
The most common osmotic diuretic used to decrease ICP is...	Mannitol
The most common loop diuretic given to decrease ICP is...	Lasix (Furosemide)
The most common anti-inflammatory drug given to decrease ICP is _____.	Decadron (Dexamethasone)
If analgesia is necessary for the patient with increased ICP the doctor should order _____.	Codeine

Why is codeine alone used for analgesia in increased ICP?	Because it does not depress respiration or LOC as much as other narcotics, and it suppresses cough.

INTRACRANIAL SURGERY

Should you shampoo the scalp and hair of the patient before cranial surgery?	Yes
What should you do with the hair shaved from the scalp pre-operatively?	Save it for the patient
If surgery was supratentorial (cerebral, pituitary) position the patient _____ postoperatively.	On the back or non-operative side, with HOB up 15 to 45.
If the surgery was infratentorial (cerebellum/ brainstem) position the patient....	Keep HOB flat
Should the client turn, cough, deep breath after a craniotomy?	Turn every 2 hours, deep breathe every hour, no cough (could cause increased ICP)
Should the client with cranial surgery have fluids forced or restricted?	Restricted to 1500 ML per 24 hours.
What are three common complications of craniotomy?	Diabetes insipidus (frontal craniotomy), increased ICP, meningitis
If the postoperative craniotomy patient has a high temperature in the first 48 hours postoperatively, it is probably due to _____.	Increased ICP, especially hypothalamus (remember surgical wound infections don't occur until day 3 or 4), post operative inflammatory temperatures are not usually over 100.8°.
What drug will be used for post-operative analgesia?	Codeine
Why is the patient taking Dilantin, Phenytoin post-craniotomy?	Prevent seizures
Describe two ways to determine if drainage post-craniotomy is CSF.	Test for glucose (if positive then CSF), watch for halo effect on gauze (if present then CSF).

INTRAVENOUS PYELOGRAM

What painful procedure must occur as part of an IVP?	IV puncture
Does the client need to empty his bladder before an IVP?	Yes
Is the client NPO for an IVP?	Yes, after midnight
What subjective experience will the client have at the beginning of an IVP?	Hot flush, salty taste in mouth (these are transitory and will pass quickly).
Does the client need to have a catheter inserted for an IVP?	No
Is a dye always used during an IVP?	Yes
What structures are visualized during an IVP?	Kidneys, renal pelvis, ureters, bladder
If the client is allergic to iodine dye an IVP cannot be done. (T/F)	False, they will just give Benadryl or steroids for a few days pre-test.
What question should be asked to assess a client's risk of allergic reaction to IVP dye?	If the client is allergic to iodine or shellfish.
What is required the evening before an IVP?	An active bowel prep with laxatives (optional in infants and children).
What are important post-test measures after an IVP?	Encourage fluids, ambulate with assistance
Performance of an IVP on what group of clients is most dangerous?	Dehydrated elderly (can get renal failure)

LABORATORY VALUES

RBC	4.0 to 6.0 mil/ul
WBC	5,000 to 11,000
Platelet count	150,000 to 400,000

Creatinine	0.6 to 1.2 mg/dl
Na	135 to 145
HCO3	22 to 26
Hematocrit	36 to 54
pCO2	35 to 45
K	3.5 to 5.3
pO2	78 to 100
BUN	8 to 25 (some sources are as high as 30)
Hemoglobin	12 to 16 female; 14 to 18 male
pH	7.35 to 7.45
O2 sat	93 to 100

PEG TUBES

What does "PEG" mean?	Percutaneous endoscopic gastrostomy
What does "percutaneous" mean?	Through the skin.
What does "endoscopic" mean?	A scope that enters a body cavity is used for placement.
What does "gastrostomy" mean?	An artificially created opening of the stomach to the outside of the abdomen.
What is the primary purpose for a PEG tube?	Long-term use of an enteral feeding tube.
What does "enteral" mean?	Using the GI tract.
What should the nurse do if the PEG tube comes out?	Put it back through the hole...it is not a big deal.

Can you have a PEG tube for life?	Yes
Are patients allowed to eat when they have a PEG tube?	Yes
Can a person with a PEG tube shower?	Yes
How soon after insertion can a patient with a PEG tube shower?	After 24 hours.
Can a person with a PEG tube enter a swimming pool?	Yes!
Is a PEG tube considered to be a "life support measure"?	Yes, it is. So, to enter hospice you cannot be using one.
In what position should a patient be placed before administering a PEG tube feeding?	Mid to high Fowler's position.
How long should a person remain seated UPRIGHT after a PEG tube feeding?	For 30 minutes.
Do you have to check placement before using a PEG tube?	No, but you should check for patency with a little water.
What is the MOST common complication with a PEG tube?	Local infection at insertion site.
What signs would tell you there is an infection at the insertion site?	Painful, red, swollen site, with or without drainage.
How much fluid do you flush a PEG tube with?	30mL
When does the nurse flush a PEG tube?	Before and after each feeding.
What is a typical bolus (all at once) feeding volume for an adult?	200-250 mL.
How soon can a nurse feed a patient through a PEG tube after insertion?	As soon as 2 hours after insertion, a nurse can feed through the tube.

POST-OPERATIVE CARE

How often should the client cough and deep breathe post-operatively?	Every 2 hours
How often should the post-operative patient turn?	Every 2 hours
How often should the patient use the incentive spirometer?	Every 1 to 2 hours
How often should the nurse auscultate the lung sounds post-operatively?	Every 4 hours
How often should the bedridden postoperative patient do leg exercises?	Every 2 hours
The post-operative patient should void by ___ hours post-operatively or you must call the HCP.	6 to 8
Will the typical post-operative client have lung sounds? Bowel sounds? Increased temperature?	Lung--yes; bowel sounds--no; Low grade temperature--yes
Unless contraindicated, the patient should be out of bed no later than ___ hours postoperatively.	24
Deep vein thrombosis is most common in what type of surgery?	Low abdominal or pelvic
The most common complication of deep vein thrombosis is _____ _____.	Pulmonary embolism
The best way to prevent thrombophlebitis is TED hose. (T/F)	False, ambulation/exercise are the best way.
What is paralytic ileus?	Paralysis of the bowel due to surgery (Common--especially in abdominal surgery).
If a postoperative patient complains of gas and cramping, you should first _____ then ____.	Assess then ambulate
The typical post-operative inflammatory temperature elevation is in the range of _____.	99.8° to 101°

The onset of post operative infection is on the _____ or _____ day postoperative day.	2nd or 3rd, never before that (remember elevated temperatures earlier than the 2nd postoperative day is not infection).
Define dehiscence.	Separation of the incisional edges
Define evisceration.	Protrusion of abdominal contents through a dehiscence.
What do you do for dehiscence?	Decrease HOB (but not flat); can steri strip, then call HCP.
What do you do, in order, for evisceration?	Decrease HOB (but not flat); cover with sterile gauze moistened with sterile saline, call HCP.

PYLORIC STENOSIS

Where is the pyloric sphincter?	At the distal (duodenal) end of the stomach
What does stenosis mean?	Narrowed
What is done to correct pyloric stenosis?	Surgery (pyloromyotomy)
In what position should the child with PS be during feeding?	High fowler's
The feedings for an infant with pyloric stenosis should be thick or thin?	Thickened
What test is done to confirm a diagnosis of pyloric stenosis?	Upper GI series (barium swallow)
These infants are prone to develop_____ and failure to _____.	Dehydration, thrive
Why does the pyloric valve become stenosed in this disease?	It hypertrophies
In what position should a child be after a feeding?	Right side with HOB up
The infant appears _____ even after vomiting.	Hungry

What do you see during and after feeding?	Peristaltic waves from left to right
Is the vomiting projectile or non-projectile? Is the vomiting bile-stained or not bile stained?	Projectile, not bile-stained
What assessment finding is found under the right rib cage?	An olive-sized bulge (the hypertrophied pylorus)
The symptoms of pyloric stenosis mostly commonly appear at age ___ to ____.	4 to 6 weeks
Describe the typical child with pyloric stenosis.	Firstborn, full term, white, boys

RECOVERY ROOM

In the recovery room (PACU), the patient should be positioned . . .	On either side
What reflex is commonly routinely tested in the recovery room?	Gag reflex
When will the artificial airway be removed in the recovery room?	When the gag reflex returns
Vital signs are measured _____ in the recovery room.	Every 15 minutes
In the recovery room the head should be...	To the side with the cheek and neck extended slightly down.
In the recovery room the neck should be?	Slightly extended
Can post-operative pain medications be given in the recovery room?	Yes

SPINAL TAP VIA LUMBAR PUNCTURE

What is the purpose of restricting activity after spinal tap?	To prevent headache due to CSF loss.

Should the client drink after a spinal tap?	Yes, encourage fluids to replace CSF.
Do you need an informed consent for a spinal tap?	Yes
Should CSF contain blood?	No
Does the client have to be NPO before a spinal tap?	No
What is the normal color of cerebrospinal fluid?	Clear, colorless
Into what space is the needle inserted during a spinal tap?	Subarachnoid space
Can the client turn side-to-side after a spinal tap?	Yes
In what position should the client be during a spinal tap?	Lateral decubitus (on their side) position and knees to chest
Identify the activity restriction necessary after lumbar puncture?	Lie flat for 6 to 12 hours
What are the two purposes of a spinal tap?	To measure or relieve pressure and obtain a CSF sample
Does the client have to be sedated before a spinal tap?	No

SUCTIONING OF THE AIRWAY

Which hand should hold the suction catheter? Which should hold the connecting tube?	The dominant, the non-dominant
The nurse should use (medical/surgical) asepsis during airway suction?	Surgical asepsis (sterile technique)
What kind of lubricant should be used on the suction catheter?	Sterile water-soluble

Should the suction be continuous or intermittent?	Intermittent to prevent mucosal damage
For how long should suction be applied during any one entry of the catheter?	10 seconds
How often should the nurse clear the tubing during suctioning?	After each pass/entry/removal
Which way would you turn the client head to suction the right mainstem bronchus? The left mainstem bronchus?	To the left, to the right
The best client position during airway suctioning is _____.	Semi-fowlers
The suction should be delivered while (inserting/removing) the catheter.	While removing the catheter
What outcomes would indicate that suctioning was effective?	Clear even lung sounds, normal vital signs
How often should the client's airway be suctioned?	When it needs to be, for example moist lung sounds, tachycardia, restlessness (hypoxia), ineffective cough.
The unconscious client should assume what position during suctioning?	Side-lying facing nurse
If not contraindicated, what action by the nurse before suctioning would most likely reduce hypoxia during suctioning?	Administer a few breaths at 100% oxygen before beginning
What solution should be used to clear the tubing during suctioning?	Sterile saline
With what size catheter should an adult's airway be suctioned?	12 to 16 French
How much suction should be used for an infant?	Less than 80 mm Hg
How much suction should be used for a child?	80 to 100 mm Hg
How much suction should be used for an adult?	120 to 150 mm Hg

TED'S and SCD's

What does TED mean?	Thrombo-embolic-deterrent. It means prevents clots and emboli.
In what form do TED's come?	They are stockings to be worn on the lower extremities.
What does SCD mean?	Sequential compression device.
What is the primary purpose of SCD's?	To milk the venous blood back out of the legs so venous pooling is prevented.
In what form do SCD's come?	They are two plastic pads that wrap around the legs attached to a device that pumps air to inflate and deflate the pads to "milk" the venous blood up the legs.
What is another name for TED's?	Compression stockings.
To apply TED's the patient should be in the _____ position.	Supine
Are wrinkles allowed in proper TED use?	No
Ted hose are most effective when placed in the _____ before the patient _____.	Morning, rises.
If the patient's skin need relief from TED hose compression it is best to remove the TED's _____.	At bedtime.
Can a person wear socks over TED's?	Yes
Can you wash TED's and reuse?	Absolutely. It is recommended that a patient have two pair so they can be laundered.
The best way to dry Ted's is to let them _____ dry on a towel.	Air. If a patient uses a dryer to dry the TED's, it needs to be on the lowest heat setting.
Should a nurse or UAP wear gloves when putting TEDs on a patient?	Yes

The term venous thromboembolism (VTE) is used to refer to both _____ and _____ _____.	DVT (deep vein thrombosis), Pulmonary embolism (PE).
Are SCD's the BEST INITIAL therapy to prevent VTE?	Yes, better than drugs.
Can nurses put a patient on SCD's independently?	No, it requires a HCP order.
Usually SCD's are _____ high.	Knee.
If a patient already has DVT can SCD's be used?	NO... it might cause embolization.
When SCD's are being used the patient should be told to report _____ _____ _____ and any _____.	"Pins and needles" Pain
How tight should SCD's be?	The nurse should be able to slide two fingers between the SCD and the leg.
How often should the nurse remove the SCD sleeve and assess the patient?	Every 8 hours
When assessing a patient on SCD's the nurse removes the sleeves to check the _____ and _____.	Skin, Neurovascular (pulse, warmth sensation, movement etc.)
Can a patient ambulate with the SCD sleeve on?	NO, they are a trip hazard.
When should SCD's be reapplied?	Immediately after ambulation or assessment.

UPPER GI SERIES

The purpose of an upper GI series is to detect?	Ulcerations
What three structures does an upper GI series visualize?	Esophagus, stomach, duodenum
Does barium come in different flavors?	Yes
What is the most uncomfortable aspect of an upper GI series?	Lying and turning on a hard, flat X-ray table

Is fasting required before and upper GI series?	Yes, usually NPO after midnight.
How much barium is to be swallowed?	8 oz
Barium is _____ in consistency.	Chalky--bitter taste
If an ulceration does not reduce by 50% on upper GI in 3 weeks of medication treatment, then _____ is suspected.	Malignancy

VITAL SIGNS

What are the three classic vital signs?	Temperature, pulse, respiration
Measurement of vitals requires a doctor's orders. (T/F)	FALSE
The temperature of the extremities and skin is (higher/lower) than the core.	Lower
List the five most common sites in which to measure the temperature.	Oral, axillary, rectal, tympanic, temporal
The normal adult temperature via the oral route is....	98.6°
The normal rectal temperature is....	99.6°
The normal axillary temperature is....	97.6°
Body temperature is (increased/decreased) with activity.	Increased
With any oral temperature device, the meter must be _____ the _____, and the _____ must be _____.	Under, tongue, mouth, closed
If your client is 4 years old or younger, should you take an oral temperature?	No
Can you measure an oral temperature on an unconscious client?	No

Can you measure an oral temperature on someone with an NG tube in place?	No
If the client is found smoking, eating or drinking when you are about to take a temperature you should wait _____ (at least).	15 minutes
Should you use the oral route for measuring temperature when a client has oxygen per nasal cannulae?	Yes
People on seizure precaution should have their temperature measured by which route?	Rectal or axillary, tympanic or tempora, dermal
People with facial trauma should have their temperature measured by which route?	Rectal or axillary or tympanic, dermal
Clients, after rectal surgery, should have their temperatures measured by which route?	Oral, axillary, tympanic or temporal
Is it acceptable practice to count the number of respirations in 15 seconds and multiply by 4 to get the rate (T/F)	Yes, if the respirations are regular.
People with heart blocks or conduction problems should not have their temperatures taken per ____. Why?	Rectum--vagal stimulation causes more heart block.
In the normal adult, which is longer, inspiration or expiration?	Expiration
What is the normal respiratory rate for an adult?	12 to 20
What is bradypnea?	Any respiratory rate below 10 per minute.
What is tachypnea?	Any respiratory rate above 24 per minute.
What is the pulse?	The surge of blood ejected from the left ventricle.
What is the average pulse rate for an adult?	72 per minute (60 to 100)

What rate classifies as tachy in an adult?	A rate above 100 per minute
What rate classifies as brady in an adult?	A rate below 60 per minute
Will pain alone increase the pulse rate?	Yes
Which finger should never be used to determine a pulse?	The thumb
What does it mean to measure an apical pulse?	To auscultate with a stethoscope over the chest to hear the heart rate.
If a pulse is irregular, how would you determine the rate?	Feel/listen for 30 seconds and multiply by 2.
If an apical/radial pulse is regular, how would you determine the rate?	Count for 30 seconds and multiply by 2.
What is an apical-radial pulse?	When two nurses measure the apical rate simultaneously with the radial rate for comparison.
How long must an apical-radial pulse be measured?	Always for 1 full minute
How many nurses are needed to measure an apical-radial pulse?	Always two (it is never acceptable for one nurse to measure the apical pulse for a minute and then measure the radial for a minute).

VOIDING CYSTOGRAM

What is a voiding cystogram?	It is a series of X-rays taken as the person with a full bladder is asked to void. The Xrays show any reflux of urine back up the ureters (a dye was injected prior to this).
Does the client need to have a catheter inserted for a voiding cystogram?	Yes
Is the client sedated for a voiding cystogram?	No
Is the client NPO for a voiding cystogram?	No, just clear liquid breakfast.
What problems does a voiding cystogram diagnose best?	Bladder filling problems, vesicoureteral reflux
What precautions are necessary for males during a voiding cystogram?	Shielding the testicles from the X-rays
Is there a bowel evacuation prep for a voiding cystogram?	No

CHAPTER 8

PHYSIOLOGICAL ADAPTATION

ACUTE GLOMERULAR NEPHRITIS (AGN)

Acute Glomerular nephritis is an_____ of the _____ most often due to _____.	Inflammation, Basement membrane of the kidney, antigen/antibody reaction.
What is the typical description of urine with AGN?	Dark tea colored urine.
What happens to the kidney in AGN?	It becomes clogged with antigen-antibody complexes which then cause inflammation and loss of function.
What are the first signs of AGN?	Puffiness of face, dark urine
Is dietary protein limited in AGN?	Not usually – however if there is severe azotemia then it may be restricted –azotemia means nitrogenous wastes in the blood – increased creatinine, BUN.
What is the best indicator of renal function?	The serum creatinine (the GFR, glomerular filtration rate is actually better, but way more expensive).
AGN has a poor prognosis (T/F)	False, the vast majority of clients recover completely from it.
How can AGN be prevented?	By having all sore throats cultured for strep and treating any strep infections.
What is the most important intervention in treating AGN?	Bedrest – they can walk if hematuria, edema, and hypertension are gone.
What is the most common dietary restriction for AGN?	Moderate sodium restriction. Fluid restriction is #2 if edema is severe
What are the urinalysis findings in AGN?	Hematuria, usually found only in diseases ending in –itis Proteinuria +3 to +4 Specific gravity up
How long after strep infection does AGN develop?	2 to 3 weeks after initial infection
How do you assess fluid excess in the child with AGN?	Daily weight

What organism causes acute glomerular nephritis?	Group A beta hemolytic strep
How often are vital sign measurements taken in AGN?	Q 4 hours with blood pressure
Will the client have hypo or hypertension with AGN? Why?	Hypertension, because of fluid retention

ANEURYSM

An aneurysm is an abnormal ____ of the wall of a(n) (artery or vein).	Widening (it is also weakening), artery
What artery is widened in a thoracic aneurysm?	The aorta
Can an aneurysm result from an infection? From syphilis?	Yes Yes
The most common symptom of abdominal aneurysm is _____.	A pulsating mass above the umbilicus.
Which aneurysm is most likely to have no symptoms...abdominal or thoracic?	The abdominal is most often "silent", ie, no symptoms.
Which vital signs are most important to measure in clients with aneurysm?	The pulse and blood pressure
An aneurysm will most affect which of the following...the blood pressure or the pulse?	The pulse – many times the aneurysm will rupture, and much blood will be lost before the blood pressure starts to change.
What activity order is the client with an aneurysm supposed to have?	BEDREST – do not get these clients up
If the client with aneurysm is physically unstable, should you encourage turning, coughing, and deep breathing?	NO – no turning, coughing, or deep breathing until the client is stable.
What class of drugs is the client with an aneurysm most likely to be on?	Antihypertensives

What is the BIG danger with aneurysms of any type?	Rupture – leads to shock and death.
If an aneurysm ruptured, how would you know it?	Decreased LOC (restlessness), Tachycardia (increased pulse rate), Hypotension (these are signs of shock) REMEMBER tachycardia occurs **before** hypotension.
If an aneurysm ruptured what is the #1 priority?	Get them to the operating room ASAP
Is there anything that can be done for the client with a ruptured aneurysm before they get to the operating room?	Yes – if available, you can get them into anti-shock trousers BUT not if this causes a delay in getting them to the operating room.
The post-op thoracic aneurysm is most likely to have which type of tube?	Chest tube, because the chest was opened
The post-op abdominal aneurysm repair client is most likely to have which type of tube?	NG tube for decompression of bowel
If you care for a client who is post-op for a repair of a femoral/popliteal resection what assessment must you make every hour for the first 24 hours?	Check the distal extremity for color, temperature, pain, and PULSE, also must document

ANGINA PECTORIS

What causes angina pectoris?	An imbalance of oxygen supply and oxygen demand of the myocardium. So, it could be due to not enough oxygen or too high of a demand on the heart to work.
Describe the pain of angina pectoris	Crushing substernal chest pain that may radiate.
What drug treats angina pectoris?	Nitroglycerin
How do you tell if the client has angina or an MI?	The pain of the two is very similar; the way to tell the difference is if nitroglycerine and rest relieve the pain, it's angina. If nitroglycerine and rest do not relieve the pain, it's probably an MI.
How many nitroglycerin tabs can you take before you call the doctor?	One tablet. The patient should take three tablets but call the doctor after one.

How many minutes should lapse between the nitroglycerin pills you take?	Five minutes, remember you can take up to 3 nitroglycerin tablets 5 minutes apart. If no relief after the first one, call MD/Squad.
By what route do you take nitroglycerin?	Sublingual
What is the action of nitroglycerin?	Dilates coronary arteries to increase blood supply and **reduces preload** (decreases workload of the heart).
What are the top 2 side effects of nitroglycerin?	Headache and hypotension
What bad thing could be occurring if a patient does not get a headache with nitroglycerin?	The nitroglycerin may be expired and inactive. They need to buy a new bottle.
In what type of container should nitroglycerin tablets be stored?	Dark, light proof container
Nitroglycerin (NTG) will (lower/raise) the blood pressure?	Lower, teach get up slowly to prevent falls
What precaution must the nurse take when administering topical nitroglycerin paste?	Wear gloves – nurse may get a dose of the medicine
NTG is an anticoagulant. (T/F)	FALSE
Everyone with angina needs bypass surgery (T/F)	FALSE

APPENDICITIS

Appendicitis is an _____ of the appendix due to _____.	Inflammation, obstruction
Appendicitis occurs most in what age group?	15 to 35
What is the most common complication of appendicitis?	Peritonitis
What is the first sign of appendicitis?	Periumbilical pain (around the navel)
What follows the periumbilical abdominal pain of appendicitis?	Nausea and vomiting

Where does the pain of appendicitis finally end up?	Right lower quadrant
What is the name of the right lower quadrant (RLQ) abdominal pain where appendicitis pain finally localizes?	McBirney's point
What is present when rebound tenderness is present?	Peritoneal inflammation
When the pain of appendicitis goes away the client is improving. (T/F)	False – rupture may have occurred
What is the highest that the temp will be in appendicitis?	102° F
What blood count is elevated in? appendicitis?	WBC
What is the name for an elevated WBC?	Leukocytosis
What is the only treatment recommended for appendicitis?	Surgery – appendectomy
Before the client with suspected appendicitis sees the physician what should be avoided?	No pain medications, NO enemas or laxatives, no food (NPO)
To lessen pain, place the client in ____ position.	Fowlers (Use post-operatively also)
Never apply ____ to the area of the appendix.	Heat, it causes rupture
After appendectomy, document in the nurses notes the return of _____.	Bowel sounds (peristalsis)

BELL'S PALSY

What cranial nerve is affected in Bell's Palsy?	#7, facial nerve
What is the #1 symptom of Bell's Palsy?	One-sided (unilateral) facial paralysis

Complete recovery from the paralysis of Bell's Palsy should occur in __ to __ months.	4 to 6 months
In addition to facial paralysis, the sense of _____ is also affected.	Taste
Will the patient be able to close their eye on the affected side?	No
Give three eye interventions for the client with Bell's Palsy.	Dark glasses, artificial tears, cover eye at night.

BENIGN PROSTATIC HYPERTROPHY (BPH) AND PROSTATECTOMY

As the prostate enlarges it compresses the _____ and causes urinary _____.	Urethra, retention
At what age does BPH occur?	Men over 50 years of age
What does BPH stand for?	Benign Prostatic Hypertrophy
In BPH the man has (increased/decreased) frequency of urination.	Increased
In BPH the force of the urinary stream is (increased/decreased).	Decreased
The man with BPH has a _____-stream of urine.	Forked
The man with BPH has hesitancy. What does this mean?	Difficulty starting to void
Will the man with BPH have enuresis, nocturia, or hematuria?	Enuresis – no, Nocturia – yes, and Hematuria – maybe
What is the best way to screen men for BPH?	Digital rectal exam
Should fluids be forced or restricted in BPH?	Forced
What does TURP stand for?	Transurethral resection of the prostate

The most radical prostate surgery is the _____ prostatectomy.	Perineal
What type of diet is used in BPH?	Acid ash
What is the primary purpose of a 3-way continuous bladder irrigation (CBI) after TURP?	To keep the catheter clear of clots and to drain urine.
What solution is used for CBI?	Normal saline (0.9 NaCl)
How fast do you run the CBI?	At whatever rate it takes to keep the urine flowing and free of clots.
What drug is used to treat bladder spasm?	B&O suppositories
Should you take a rectal temp after? prostatectomy? Give stool softeners?	No, rectal temperature Yes, stool softeners
You should call the MD after TURP when you see _____ thick _____, _____clots, and _____ urine drainage on the dressing.	Bright thick blood, persistent clots, persistent urine on dressing (don't call MD for transitory clots and urine on dressing).
If you see an increase in the blood content of urine coming out of the catheter, you would first _____.	Pull carefully on the catheter to apply local pressure on the prostate with Foley balloons.
If you see clots in the tubing, you would first _____.	Increase the flowrate
What exercises should the post prostatectomy patient do upon discharge? Why?	Perineal exercises, start and stop stream of urine, because dribbling is a common but temporary problem post-operatively.
Will the post-prostatectomy patient be impotent?	If TURP, No impotence; If prostatectomy, Yes, impotence.

BRONCHOSCOPY

Is a bronchoscopy an invasive procedure?	Yes
A bronchoscopy directly visualizes _____, _____, and _____.	Larynx Trachea The bronchi
During a bronchoscopy, a bronchial brush is for what purpose?	To obtain cells for histology.
Can tissue biopsies be performed during a bronchoscopy?	Yes
Bronchoscopies cannot be done on people who are _____, have _____ disorders, have risk for increased _____ _____, and severe acute _____ _____.	Uncooperative. Bleeding Intracranial pressure Respiratory failure
Is general anesthesia typically used during bronchoscopy?	No. A local anesthetic is used. A conscious sedative is used to relax the patient.
Does an informed consent need to be signed before a bronchoscopy?	Yes, because it is invasive.
Is the patient NPO before a bronchoscopy?	Yes, for about 8 hours to prevent aspiration of gastric contents.
Before a bronchoscopy the nurse should assist the patient to perform _____ _____ and to remove _____.	Oral hygiene Dentures (or bridges or partial plates etc.)
Which two medications are most likely given during a bronchoscopy?	Lidocaine to anesthetize the local tissues. Propofol to consciously sedate the patient.
A bronchoscopy can be performed with the patient in the _____ position or _____ ____.	Supine Sitting up
After a patient has a bronchoscopy, the nurse notices a streak of blood on a tissue used by the patient. What should the nurse do?	Nothing except document because this is normal. But report any significant amount of blood.

If a patient is unconscious after a bronchoscopy in what position are they placed?	Side lying with HOB slightly raised.
If a patient is conscious after a bronchoscopy in which position are they placed?	Semi-Fowler's
When can a patient eat or drink after a bronchoscopy?	Once the gag reflex has returned.
The major complications for which a nurse assesses a post bronchoscopy patient are: _____, _____, _____ and _____.	Bleeding from throat Laryngospasm (stridor) Hypoxia Low grade fever
The WORST complication after a bronchoscopy is a_____.	Pneumothorax due to accidental puncture.

BUERGER'S DISEASE

What is another name for Buerger's disease?	Thromboangiitis obliterans
Which extremities are affected most often?	Lower only
Which sex does it affect most often?	Males
The group with the highest incidence of Buerger's disease is _____.	Smokers
Upon walking the patient with Buerger's experiences _____ _____.	Intermittent Claudication
What is intermittent claudication?	Pain in calf upon walking

BURNS

A first-degree burn is pale or red?	Red
A first-degree burn has vesicles? (T/F)	FALSE
A second-degree burn is pale or red?	Red
A second-degree burn is dull or shiny?	Shiny

A second-degree burn has vesicles? (T/F)	TRUE
A second-degree burn is wet or dry?	Wet
A third-degree burn is white or red?	White
A third-degree is wet or dry?	Dry
A third-degree is hard or soft?	Hard
Of first, second and third degree burns which has less pain? Why?	Third degree burns, nerve damage has occurred.
For what purpose do you use the rule of nines?	To estimate the percentage of body surface burned; is NOT used for children.
In the rule of nines, the head and neck receive _____; each arm receives _____.	9%, 9%
In the rule of nines, the front trunk gets _____, the posterior trunk gets _____, each leg gets _____, and the genitalia gets ____.	18%, 18%, 18%, 1%
What is the only IM given to a burn patient?	Tetanus toxoid-if they had a previous immunization; Tetanus antitoxin-if they have never been immunized before (or immune globulin).
In the emergent phase do you cover burns? (In the field)	Yes, with anything clean and dry.
Should you remove adhered clothing?	No
Name the 3 phases of burn.	Shock, diuretic, recovery
Fluid moves from the _____ to the _____ _____ in the shock phase.	Bloodstream, interstitial space
The shock phase of the burn is potassium increased or decreased? Why?	Increased, because of all the cells damaged the K+ is released from damaged cells.
What acid-base disorder is seen in the shock phase of a burn?	Metabolic acidosis

What is the #1 therapy in the shock phase?	Fluid replacement/resuscitation
What is the simple formula for calculating fluid replacement needs in the first 24 hours after a burn?	4 ml x Kg x % burned per day i.e.: 70 Kg with 50% burn 3 x 70 x 50 = 10,500 mL
If the MD orders 2,800 cc of fluid in the first 24 hours after a burn, one- _____ of it must be infused in the first eight hours.	Half (or 1,400 mL)
What blood value will dictate IV flow rate?	The hematocrit.
How will you know the patient has entered the fluid mobilization or diuretic phase?	The urine output will increase.
How long does the fluid mobilization or diuretic phase of a burn last?	2 to 5 days
In the diuretic phase, K+ levels fall or rise?	Fall- remember diuresis always causes hypokalemia.
If the nurse accidentally runs the IVs at the shock phase rate during the diuretic phase the patient will experience ____ _____.	Pulmonary edema
The burn patient will be on _____ urine output and daily _____.	Hourly, weight
Sulfamylon cream causes the patient to experience what?	A burning sensation
Silver nitrate cream _____ the _____.	Stains, skin
Pain medication should be administered _____ minutes before _____ care.	30 minutes, wound care
When using silver nitrate on a burn, the dressing must be kept _____.	Wet
What is Curling's ulcer? Why do burn patients get it? What drug prevents it?	It is a stress GI ulcer that you get with any severe physical stress. It is prevented with H2 receptor antagonist (-tidine) and proton pump inhibitors (-zole).

CANCER FACTS

"Neoplasm" refers to both benign and malignant tumors. (T/F)	TRUE
Which type of tumor is more likely malignant? Differentiated or Undifferentiated?	Undifferentiated is worse (highly differentiated is best to have).
When cancer spreads to a distant site it is called _____?	Metastasis
The cause of cancer is known. (T/F)	Partially true, but we still don't know a lot.
A person should have a yearly exam with cancer detection over the age of?	40
In general, cancer drugs have side effects in which three body systems?	GI, hematologic (blood), integumentary (skin)
What are the three most common chemotherapy GI side effects?	Nausea and vomiting, diarrhea, stomatitis (oral sores)
Clients receiving chemotherapy must be NPO. (T/F)	FALSE
It is permissible to give Lidocaine viscous before meals if the patient has painful stomatitis. (T/F)	TRUE
With what solution should the client with stomatitis rinse after meals?	Hydrogen peroxide
Name the 3 hematologic side effects of chemotherapy.	Thrombocytopenia, leukopenia, anemia
Which cells are low in thrombocytopenia?	Platelets
What drug should not be given to the patient with chemotherapeutic thrombocytopenia?	ASA (aspirin)
When should the nurse withhold IM injections in the client on chemotherapy?	Only when their platelet count is down.

What are the 3 objective symptoms/signs of thrombocytopenia?	Epistaxis, ecchymosis, petechiae
What is epistaxis?	Nose bleeds
What is ecchymosis?	Bruising
What is petechiae?	Small dot-like pinpoint hemorrhages on the skin
What blood cell is low in leukopenia?	White blood cells
When the Absolute Neutrophil Count ANC is below _____ the person on chemotherapy will be placed on reverse isolation.	500
What is the #1 integumentary side effect of chemotherapy?	Alopecia
What is alopecia?	Hair loss
Hair loss due to chemotherapy is usually temporary. (T/F)	TRUE
Can scalp tourniquets prevent chemotherapy alopecia?	In some cases, yes
Can ice packs to the scalp prevent chemotherapy alopecia?	In some cases, yes

CATARACTS

Define cataract.	Opacity of the crystalline lens
Is surgery done immediately upon diagnosis of cataract?	No, they usually wait until it interferes with activities of daily living.
What three most common visual defects occur with cataract?	Cloudiness, diplopia (double vision), photophobia (sensitivity to light)
What are the two common treatments of cataract?	Laser, surgical removal. Surgery called intraocular or extraocular lens extraction

What does the eye look like when a client has cataracts?	Cloudy, milky-white pupil
What will the client be wearing after cataract removal?	A protective patch/shield on the operative eye for 24 hours, then a metal shield (AT NIGHT only) for 3 weeks.
When the client asks about the use of glasses or contacts after cataract surgery what would you say?	If an intraocular lens is implanted, they will NOT need glasses. If no lens is implanted, then contacts will be fitted 3 months post operatively.
What will be a high priority nursing diagnosis for a client post cataract surgery?	Safety
Should the client ambulate independently after cataract surgery?	No, depth perception is altered.
What positions are to be avoided after cataract surgery?	Lying face down. Also, do not lie on operative side for a month.
What are the postoperative signs of hemorrhage into the eye?	Severe pain, restlessness
What movements are to be avoided after cataract surgery?	Coughing, sneezing, bending at the waist, straining at stool, rubbing or touching eyes, rapid head movements.
What positions are okay after cataract surgery?	Do not lie on the operative side; do lie on your back.
Should you use talcum powder with a post operative cataract client?	No, may cause sneezing; also, should avoid pepper.
What are the three signs of increased intraocular pressure?	Pain (moderate to severe), restlessness, increased pulse rate.
What is a major objective in caring for a client after surgical cataract removal?	To prevent pressure in or on the eyes.
When the lens is to be extracted for cataract what drugs are given preoperatively?	Mydriatics, dilators, antibiotic drugs (eye drops)

What three drugs are given post-operatively?	Stool softeners, antiemetics, analgesics (mild to moderate)
Give five causes of cataract?	Injury, congenital, exposure to heat, heredity, age

CEREBROVASCULAR ACCIDENT—CVA

A CVA is a _____ of brain cells due to decreased _____ _____ and _____.	Destruction; blood flow and oxygen
Women have a (higher/lower) incidence of stroke than men?	Lower
Name the three types of CVA.	Embolus, thrombus, hemorrhage
Use of oral contraceptives increases the risk of CVA. (T/F)	TRUE
Chronic abuse of alcohol increases the risk of CVA. (T/F)	FALSE
Obesity increases the risk of CVA. (T/F)	TRUE
Smoking increases the risk of CVA. (T/F)	TRUE
Atrial fibrillation increases the risk of CVA. (T/F)	True, emboli particularly
What is TIA?	Transient ischemic attack, warning sign of impending CVA (transient neurologic deficits of any kind can last 30 seconds to 24 hours).
Do patients experiencing a CVA have a headache?	Yes
The first sign of CVA is usually a _____.	Change in LOC
The activity order in early management of CVA is _____.	Absolute bed rest
The patient with a recent CVA is most likely to have fluids restricted or forced?	Restricted
How far should the HOB be up after CVA?	30°

Can the stroke victim be turned side-to-side?	Yes
How often should the CVA patient be turned and repositioned?	Every 2 hours
The CVA patient should be turned onto his paralyzed side no longer than 2 hours. (T/F)	False, the patient should not be on their paralyzed side for more than 20 minutes.
ROM exercises should occur every 2 hours. (T/F)	False-every four hours or three times a day is enough.
To prevent urinary incontinence, the CVA patient should be catheterized. (T/F)	False-remember incontinence will never be allowed as a reason for catheterization.
Which type of paralysis is typical of CVA paraplegia, hemiplegia or quadriplegia?	Hemiplegia
What anatomical fact accounts for the left side of the body being controlled by the right brain?	The motor-pyramidal-tracts cross over to the other side (decussate in the medulla).
If the patient has right hemiplegia, he cannot move his _____ and _____ the stroke was on the _____ side of the brain.	Right arm, right leg, left
What is hemianopsia?	Not being able to see ½ of the field of vision
The client with hemianopsia should be taught to _____.	Scan
What is scanning?	Moving the head from side to side to see the whole field of vision.
If the client has right homonymous hemianopsia, the food on the _____ side of the tray may be ignored.	Right
After meals the nurse must always check ____ of the CVA client for _____.	Mouth (or cheek); food
Should a CVA patient always have all four side rails up? Should they be restrained?	Top side rails, yes. Restraints no-unless they are a danger to self or others.

When a patient does not understand incoming language, he is said to have _____ aphasia.	Receptive
When the CVA client understands your question but can't respond verbally correctly, he is said to have _____ aphasia.	Expressive
What is global aphasia?	Both receptive and expressive.
Aphasia is most common if the stroke occurred in the (dominant/non-dominant) hemisphere of the brain.	Dominant
How do you tell which side of the person's brain is dominant?	It is the side that controls their dominant hand, i.e., a left-handed person has a dominant right hemisphere and conversely a right-hand person has a dominant left hemisphere.
For which type of aphasia are slow, short, simple directions most useful?	Receptive
For which type of aphasia is careful listening and needs anticipation most useful?	Expressive
The loss of the ability to perform purposeful, skilled acts, i.e., brushing teeth, is called _____.	Apraxia

CHEST PT AND ISE

What does Chest PT (CPT) stand for?	Chest Physical Therapy
What is another name for CPT?	Postural drainage
For what disease is CPT most frequently performed?	Cystic Fibrosis
The purpose of CPT is to _____ the _____ of _____ from all _____ lobes.	Drain Lung Mucus Five
What force is used to remove the mucus from the lungs in CPT?	Gravity, no suction is used.

How does CPT use gravity to remove mucus from the lungs?	The client is placed in five positions to drain the mucus.
What is the meaning of PD & P?	Postural drainage and PERCUSSION.
How does the nurse perform percussion?	To clap on the client's chest wall over the lung lobes using a cupped hand.
What is the purpose of percussion?	To loosen mucus secretions from the walls on the airways so the lobes drain more completely and easily.
What type of vest is usually worn during CPT?	A vibration vest the loosen the mucus from the walls of the airways.
Can CPT be performed by family and caregivers in the home?	Yes, with appropriate and effective teaching and learning.
What areas of the chest wall should be avoided when performing percussion?	Spine, stomach, sternum, and lower ribs.
How long does CPT take to perform?	30-40 minutes
What MUST be done whenever position is changed in CPT?	Have the patient cough out the drained mucus.
How many position changes are there in CPT?	5 to 9
What is the meaning of ISE?	Incentive spirometry exercises.
In what situation is ISE used most frequently?	For pulmonary function after surgery.
A typical ISE device has _____ chamber, each containing a small _____ that _____ when the client _____.	Three Ball Rises Inhales
The purpose of ISE is to_____ _____ the _____.	Fully Expand Lungs
It is important to teach the patient to _____ NOT _____ when doing ISE'S.	Inhale Exhale

How often should a patient perform ISE's post-surgery?	Every hour while awake.
How many inhalation cycles (reps) should a patient do each time they exercise	Five breaths at least.
What should the patient do after fully inhaling on the spirometer?	Hold their breathe for 5-10 seconds.
What is the pattern that is repeated 5 times each exercise?	Inhale, Hold breathe...exhale.
When should a patient performing ISE's cough?	At the end of the five cycles, not after each exhale.
What should be done after the patient has finished coughing after the last exhale?	Oral hygiene.

CHRONIC OTITIS MEDIA

What is otitis media?	Chronic infectious/inflammatory disease of the middle ear.
Is otitis a disease of the adult or child?	Usually, the child
What part of the ear is involved in otitis media?	Middle ear
What are the 2 common subjective signs of otitis media?	Hearing loss, feeling of fullness in the ear.
What are the 2 objective signs of otitis media?	Hyperpyrexia (fever), drainage from the ear.
What commonly happens secondary to otitis media?	Perforation of the eardrum
Do all the children with otitis media need tubes in their ears?	No

What are the two most common medical treatments for otitis media?	Systemic antibiotics, antibiotic ear drops
What is the most severe complication of otitis media?	Meningitis or mastoiditis
What is cholesteatoma?	An epidermal cyst in the ear
What are the restrictions to be followed when tubes are in a child's ear?	No swimming, no showering, no diving

CLEFT LIP AND PALATE

What is a cleft lip?	The lip is open to the nares.
What is a cleft palate?	The roof of the mouth is open to the nasopharynx.
Is it possible to have only one: cleft lip or cleft palate?	Yes, you can have one or the other or both.
When will the cleft lip be repaired?	Between 10 weeks and 6 months
When is cleft palate repaired?	Between 1 and 5 years of age
Why is cleft lip repaired early? (2 reasons)	Feeding is easier after repair and appearance after repair is more acceptable to parents.
Describe the nipples on bottles used to feed babies with cleft lip.	Large-holed, soft nipples
The infant with cleft lip/cleft palate needs more frequent _____.	Bubbling/burping
Children with cleft lip/palate should be fed in what position?	An almost upright position
What is the #1 complication of cleft lip/palate?	Aspiration
Children with cleft lip and cleft palate have long-term problems with _____, _____, and _____.	Hearing, speech, teeth

In how many surgeries is the cleft palate repaired?	Two surgeries-one at 12 to 18 months, the last at 4 to 5 years.
Why is final repair of the palate delayed until 4 to 5 years of age?	Earlier surgery would interfere with tooth development
How are cleft lip and cleft palate primarily treated?	Surgical repair
Is the infant restrained before repair?	No, just after repair.
Should children with cleft palate before surgery be allowed to cry? To breast-feed?	Yes, they can cry; may breast-feed with a simple cleft lip however palate interferes with feeding.
After repairing the cleft lip, is the infant allowed to cry? To breast-feed?	No, the infant should be held to prevent crying; the infant is not allowed to breastfeed because sucking is not good after lip repair.
After cleft lip repair, what device will the baby wear?	A Logan bow.
What is the purpose of a Logan Bow?	To prevent stress on the suture line.
With what device will the infant be restrained after repair?	Elbow restraints
How do you care for an infant with a Logan Bow?	Remove the gauze before feeding and cleanse after feeding with peroxide and saline.
Can cleft lip/palate babies sleep on their backs?	Yes

What position is contraindicated after cleft lip repair?	Never lie on their abdomen
What will be used to feed the infant after cleft lip repair?	A dropper/syringe with rubber tip to discourage sucking.
What must the mother do after feeding the baby who has had cleft lip/palate repair?	Rinse the infant's/child's mouth with water.

COLOSTOMY

What is a colostomy?	A surgically created opening of the colon out onto the abdomen wall.
Name the 3 **most common** reasons for a colostomy.	Cancer, diverticulitis, ulcerative colitis
What is meant by the term "temporary" colostomy?	A colostomy that is not intended to be permanent-the bowel will be reconnected at a later date and the client will defecate normally.
What is meant by the term "double barrel" colostomy?	A procedure where the colon is cut and both ends are brought out onto the abdomen.
Colostomies performed for cancer tend to be (temporary/permanent).	Permanent
Colostomies performed for a gunshot are usually (temporary/permanent).	Temporary
In a double-barrel colostomy, from which stoma (barrel) will the stool come out?	Proximal
A fresh new stoma is _____, _____, and _____.	Red, large, noisy
When a client voices embarrassment over the noises that their colostomy makes on the first post-op day, what would you say?	The noise will go away in a few days to a week.

What behavior on the part of the client is the BEST indicator that they have accepted their stoma?	When they do their own stoma care.
By what day post-op should the client begin to take care of their own stoma?	By the 3rd to 4th day, they should be looking at it and asking questions by day 2.
The more colon is removed the more _____ the stool.	Liquid
What technique is used to remove feces and flatus from the bowel through a colostomy?	Colostomy irrigation
How many times per day will the client irrigate his colostomy?	Once
Which solution is used to irrigate a colostomy?	Tap water
How warm should the irrigation solution be?	Warmer than body temp., i.e., 99º-100º F
In what position should the client be when they irrigate their colostomy?	Sitting

CONGESTIVE HEART FAILURE—CHF

CHF can be right-sided, left-sided, or both-sided. (T/F)	True, left-sided usually comes first.
What does right-sided CHF mean?	Right ventricle has decompensated
What does left-sided CHF mean?	Left ventricle has decompensated
CHF can result from MI. (T/F)	TRUE
When cardiac output fails, name three ways the heart will try to compensate.	Ventricles will hypertrophy, dilate and heart rate will increase.
What is meant by "cardiac decompensation"?	It means that the compensatory mechanisms--hypertrophy, dilation, tachycardia are not working, and the heart has failed.

Name the three groups of drugs used to treat CHF?	Diuretics, digitalis, vasodilators
What is the activity order for clients with decompensated CHF?	Bed rest
What special item do clients with CHF have to wear to decrease venous stasis in the legs?	TED hose
How often should anti-embolism hose (TED) be removed?	Daily
When during the day should TED hose be applied?	Before the client gets out of bed
Should you massage the calves of the client with CHF?	Never
Before you give digitalis, what action must you take?	Measure the apical pulse.
If the adult client's apical pulse is below 60, what should you do?	Do not give digitalis--for a child don't give if pulse under 70; for an infant don't give for a pulse under 90.
What daily measurement best indicates the amount of fluid the client is retaining?	Daily weight
Should clients with CHF have a Foley catheter?	Yes, on diuretics and fluid balance is important.
What complication is common in CHF?	Pulmonary edema.

When the client is taking diuretics, what mineral is the CHF client most likely to lose?	Potassium--K+
You should tell the client with CHF to immediately report to his doctor if he gains _____ pound in one week.	Three pounds.
Name the four most common toxic effects of digitalis.	Anorexia, N & V--very common, yellow vision, arrhythmia.

CUSHINGS SYNDROME

Cushings syndrome is _____ secretion of _____, _____ and _____ _____ by the _____ _____.	Over secretion; glucocorticoids, mineralocorticoids, androgenic hormones, adrenal gland.
In Cushings the blood sugar is (increased/ decreased).	Increased
In Cushings syndrome, the client develops _____ face.	Moon
In Cushings syndrome, the trunk is _____ and the extremities are _____.	Obese, thin
What is seen on the abdomen of the patient with Cushings?	Striae--purple horizontal lines
Emotional changes with Cushings are _____and _____.	Emotional labile, depression
Men with Cushings develop _____.	Gynecomastia
What is gynecomastia?	Female-type breasts
Women with Cushings develop _____.	Hirsutism, amenorrhea
What is hirsutism?	Hair where you don't want it.
The Cushings syndrome patient will have a _____ _____ on their upper back.	Buffalo hump

The patient with Cushings will have (increased /decreased) blood pressure.	Increased, remember retaining water and sodium.
The Cushings syndrome patient will have _____ natremia, _____ kalemia, and _____ glycemia.	Hyper; Hypo; Hyper
Cushings clients will have (increased/ decreased) resistance to infection.	Decreased
Chronic _____ therapy imitates Cushings.	Steroid
Cushings man--moon face with infection and buffalo hump on back, big trunk, thin extremities, loses potassium, keeps glucose, salt, has striations on abdomen, and breasts. (T/F)	TRUE

CYSTIC FIBROSIS—CF

Is CF hereditary?	Yes
What glands are affected in CF?	Exocrine glands
What is the appearance of the stool in a client with CF?	Fat, frothy, foul-smelling, floating, steatorrhea
What are the top 2 nursing diagnoses for a client with CF?	Decreased airway clearance; Alteration in nutrition or alteration in absorption.
What is the classic test for CF?	Iontophoresis--sweat test
In which two systems/organs are the most problems in CF?	Lungs, pancreas
How does the client evaluate the activity of their pancreas?	Observe stools for steatorrhea
What is the typical diet for the CF client?	High calorie, high protein, modified fat
The major problem in CF is _____.	Increased viscosity of the secretions of exocrine glands lead to obstruction.

The most common intervention for the CF clients with a diagnosis of decreased airway clearance is _____.	Postural drainage.
What vitamins need to be replaced in CF?	Fat soluble in water soluble form--A, D, E, K
What do CF clients need to do (ingest) in hot weather?	Take NaCl tablets
The child with a diagnosis of CF probably had a history of _____ _____ at birth.	Meconium ileus--bowel obstruction due to the thickness of the stool.
Why is the child with CF receiving pancreas/viokase/pancreatin?	They are enzymes which aid absorption of nutrients.
When should the child with CF take his pancreatin/viokase/pancreas?	With meals, so it is in the gut while the food is present, the whole purpose is to increase absorption of ingested food.

DETACHED RETINA

What is the most important thing to do immediately when retinal detachment is suspected?	Bedrest
Define detached retina.	Separation of the retina from the back of the eye--the choroid.
What is the most common complication of retinal reattachment?	Hemorrhage
What group of drugs are given to people with retinal detachment?	Tranquilizers
What is the most common visual defect with retinal detachment?	A veil or curtain in the line of sight.
Give three common causes of retinal detachment.	Trauma, aging, cataract surgery
Does the client always need surgery for retinal detachment?	No, lasers can be used, as can freezing probes.

Will the client's eyes be bandaged after retinal surgery?	Both will be, also before surgery as well.
Can the client return to work after retinal surgery?	Not for 3 weeks--and may not be able to go back to active jobs 6 to 8 weeks after that.
What environmental change is most appropriate for clients after retinal reattachment?	Dimmed lighting
What are the two non-surgical treatments done for retinal detachment?	Laser photocoagulation cryosurgery-- freezing.
Give two odd visual sensations that these clients have.	Flashes of light--floaters
Name a surgical procedure done for retinal detachment.	Scleral buckling

DRAINS

The purpose of wound drains is to prevent _____ and promote _____.	Infection Healing
The three most commonly used rains are _____, _____, and _____ _____.	Penrose Hemovac Jackson Pratt (JP)
The drain that removes primarily serosanguinous fluid from between tissue layers **without suction** is a _____ drain.	Penrose
What is serosanguineous fluid?	It is a mix of serous (pink blood) cellular fluid and blood (red).
The drain that removes fluid from between tissue layers **using** gentle **suction** is a _____ drain.	Jackson Pratt (JP).
The drain that removes sanguineous fluid from tissues or cavities **using suction** is the _____ drain.	Hemovac

Hemovacs are used frequently in the post operative management of which type of surgery?	Orthopedic
How is suction generated in a Jackson Pratt?	From a collapsible plastic bulb.
How is suction generated in a hemovac?	By the expansion of a metal spring coil in the device.
Immediately after inserting or emptying a JP the bulb needs to be _____ and _____.	Flat Capped
Immediately after inserting or emptying a Hemovac drain the round collection chamber needs to be _____ and _____.	Flat Capped
How often do drains need to be emptied?	At least every 8 hours or more frequently if there is a lot of drainage?
How much drainage means the JP can come out?	25 mL or less in 8 hours.
In what direction does a nurse open the cap on a drain?	AWAY from the nurse's face. Open so any squirt goes away from the nurse.
Is emptying a drain performed as a sterile procedure?	No. Clean technique is adequate.
Can a patient's family manage drains at home?	Yes, with proper teaching and learning.
Does a penrose drain have a drainage collection chamber like a JP and Hemovac?	No, the fluid drains and collects on a dressing.
What does it mean to "advance" a penrose drain?	To pull it **out** an inch and reapply the dressing.
Should the rubber tubing of a Penrose drain be folded?	No this prevents drainage.
How is a Penrose drain secured?	With a sterile safety pin.
How is a JP drain secured?	Usually with a single stitch to the skin.

EMPHYSEMA

What position is best for clients with emphysema under normal circumstances?	Semi-fowlers or higher
What flow rates of O2 are appropriate for the client with emphysema?	Low flow-- <2.5 L/min; never exceed 2.5 L in COPD
If a client with emphysema has a severe dyspneic episode what position is best?	Sitting upright with arms folded on the overbed table.
What will you observe on the hands of the client with emphysema?	Clubbing of the fingernail beds
In emphysema, the alveoli are over- _____ and under- _____.	Over-enlarged, under-ventilated so that air is trapped in alveoli.
The development of emphysema is most associated with a history of _____.	Smoking
In emphysema, the appetite _____ the weight _____ and the anterior-post diameter of the chest _____.	Decreases, decreases, increases
What is the increase in anterior-posterior diameter of emphysema called?	Barrel chest
The persons with emphysema have _____, _____ lip and (slow/rapid) breathing.	Grunting, pursed, rapid
What dietary prescription is most appropriate for the client with emphysema?	Frequent small meals to prevent tiring
What fluid order should the emphysema client have?	3 liters of fluid per day (this is an increase)
The client with emphysema is (ruddy/pale/cyanotic).	Cyanotic

ENDOCRINE DISEASES

Cushings syndrome, Cushings disease, Cretinism, Pheochromocytoma, Conn's disease, Grave's disease, Myxedema, Acromegaly, Gigantism, Pituitary dwarfism, Addison's disease

Hyperthyroid (give another name)	Grave's disease
High growth hormone in a child (give another name)	Gigantism
Over secretion of mineralocorticoids only (give another name)	Conn's disease
Low growth hormone (give another name)	Pituitary dwarfism
High growth hormone in an adult	Acromegaly
Undersecretion of adrenal cortex	Addison's disease
Hypothyroid in an adult	Myxedema/Hashimoto's
Over secretion of adrenal cortex	Cushing's syndrome
Over secretion of adrenal medulla	Pheochromocytoma
Hypothyroid in a child	Cretinism
Over secretion of ACTH	Cushing's disease

EPIGLOTTITIS

What is the #1 danger of epiglottitis?	Airway obstruction
Epiglottitis most commonly occurs in children from age _____ to _____.	1 to 8 years
What organism causes epiglottitis?	Hemophilus influenza B
What level of fever is present in epiglottitis?	Over 102°
What symptoms are classic epiglottitis?	Muffled voice, drooling, stridor
Will a child with epiglottitis cough?	NO, there will be a lack of spontaneous cough.

How will the child with epiglottitis breathe?	Leaned forward with flaring nostrils
If a child is suspected of having epiglottitis, should you put a tongue depressor in their mouth to look?	NO, never put any instrument in the child's mouth unless you are prepared to do an immediate intubation.
Would you do a throat culture?	No, never put anything in their mouth
If epiglottitis is suspected, what should the parents be told?	To take the child to the ER as soon as possible.
What drug is used to fight epiglottitis?	Penicillin, ampicillin
Children with epiglottitis often need a tracheotomy, what behavior would indicate the need for a tracheotomy?	Restlessness, increased heart rate, and retractions
What is recommended for prevention of it?	All children two months and over should receive an H. Influenzae B vaccine.

GENITAL HERPES

What type of herpes virus causes genital herpes?	Herpes simplex II
Name the two most common ways genital herpes is transmitted?	Sexual intercourse/contact; through birth.
How long is the incubation period of genital herpes?	3 to 7 days (about the same for gonorrhea)
What do lesions of herpes look like?	Fluid filled vesicles
What are the two most common sites for herpes?	On the genitals and the mouth.
What drug is used to treat herpes?	Acyclovir (or Gancyclovir, Famciclovir, Penciclovir, Valacyclovir)
The client should keep the lesions (dry/moist).	Dry
What precautions should the person with herpes take regarding sexual intercourse?	No intercourse while the vesicles are evident.

When is C-section delivery indicated if the mother is infected with herpes?	If the vesicles are present, then C-section is indicated.
How long will it take for the vesicles to heal?	Two to four weeks

GLAUCOMA

Glaucoma is an eye disorder in which there is _____ intraocular pressure in the ___ chamber.	Increased, anterior
The increase in pressure is due to an imbalance in the formation and drainage of _____ humor from the anterior chamber.	Aqueous
Glaucoma affects (one/both) eyes, usually.	Both (it is a bilateral disease)
The most common visual field defect in glaucoma is _____.	Central vision (loss of peripheral vision -- also called tunnel vision)
What are the two types of glaucoma?	Open-angle, closed angle
Which one is the typical type and the one you should know well?	Open-angle--90% of all cases
Open-angle glaucoma is seen most commonly in _____ life.	Later
Open-angle glaucoma is (painless/painful); whereas closed-angle is (painless/painful).	Open is painless; closed is painful
What drugs (class) are given to treat glaucoma?	Miotics--these constrict the pupil (remember in glaucoma DO NOT DILATE the pupil).
Name two miotics.	Pilocarpine, Timoptic (or any other drug ending in -lol)
Why is diamox given to glaucoma patients?	It is a diuretic that decreases aqueous humor production thus lowering intraocular pressure.
What type of drugs are contraindicated for glaucoma patients?	ANY drugs that dilate the pupils are BAD (i.e., mydriatics).

Can surgery be done for glaucoma?	Yes
What do you do if the patient complains of severe ocular pain after surgery?	Call the HCP--hemorrhage into the eye is most likely.

GONORRHEA

Gonorrhea is the most common venereal disease next to chlamydia. (T/F)	TRUE
Gonorrhea can infect the eyes. (T/F)	TRUE
Gonorrhea can lead to sterility (T/F)	True, in women
Gonorrhea occurs most commonly in people _____ to _____ years of age.	19 to 35
The almost exclusive way gonorrhea is transmitted to an infant's eyes is through _____.	The birth process, from mother to infant eyes.
What is the name for the gonorrhea conjunctivitis that neonates get during birth?	Ophthalmia neonatorum
In males, what is the most common sign of gonorrheal infection?	Dysuria or purulent discharge
How long is the incubation period of gonorrhea?	2 to 8 days
Which sex is most likely to be asymptomatic with gonorrhea?	Women
What is the most common symptom of gonorrhea in females?	Greenish--yellow discharge from the vagina
When does the purulent discharge of ophthalmia neonatorum begin?	2 to 3 days after birth
What is the most serious complication of ophthalmia neonatorum?	Blindness

Gonorrhea is caused by a gram (negative/positive) organism?	Negative
The drug of choice for gonorrhea is _____.	Penicillin- If resistant organism, Ciprofloxacin
Why is probenecid given before administration of penicillin?	To prevent the excretion of penicillin and thereby prolong its action.
How is the penicillin given (what route)?	IM
What is pelvic inflammatory disease?	Infection of the reproductive tract in the female, usually, but not always an advanced stage of gonorrheal infection.
How is pelvic inflammatory disease treated?	By IV penicillin
In what position should a patient with pelvic inflammatory disease be positioned?	Semi- to high- fowlers to keep the infection in the pelvis.
What drug is given to neonates to prevent gonorrheal conjunctivitis?	Erythromycin or tetracycline drops in the eyes.

GUILLAIN-BARRE SYNDROME

What is the #1 finding with Guillain-Barre?	Progressive ascending paralysis.
What causes the paralysis of GBS?	Demyelination of peripheral nerves (Unknown cause)
What kind of infection precedes Guillain Barre?	Viral
The patient completely recovers from Guillain-Barre. (T/F)	False, there are usually residual effects, but they do recover most of what was lost.
Recovery usually occurs within _____ to _____ months.	4 to 6
What is the first symptom of Guillain-Barre?	Clumsiness in ambulation (function in legs and feet is lost first).
What is the biggest danger of Guillain Barre?	Respiratory arrest secondary to diaphragmatic paralysis.

In the acute phase it is very important to assess _____ _____ every 2 hours.	Motor function of all muscles (especially the diaphragm).
Before feeding a patient with Guillain-Barre you must _____.	Check the gag reflex.
What is the most aggressive medical therapy for GBS?	Plasmapheresis--to remove antibodies from the blood.

HEMODIALYSIS

What is done in a **Graft** for hemodialysis?	A blood vessel is sutured between an artery and a vein.
Who is most likely to receive a **Graft** for dialysis?	People with diabetes mellitus.
How often do clients with renal failure undergo dialysis?	3 times per week.
Is hemodialysis short term or long term?	Both--but most short-term dialysis is achieved by hemodialysis.
How long does the average dialysis last?	4 to 6 hours
What are the 3 ways to gain access to the circulation in hemodialysis?	AV shunt, AV fistula, AV graft
What is done in an AV **Fistula**?	A surgical anastomosis is made between the artery and a vein.
Does anything exit the skin in an AV Fistula?	No
How long can an AV **Fistula** be used?	Indefinitely
What is the most common site for an AV Shunt?	Radial artery to radial vein.
What should be avoided in the arm of the client with an AV **Shunt**?	No venipuncture or blood pressure allowed in the arm with a shunt, graft, or fistula.

Does anything exit the skin in an AV Shunt?	Yes, the plastic tube that connects the artery and vein is outside the arm.
How long can an AV **Shunt** be used?	Just for a few weeks.
What syndrome results when too much fluid is exchanged during hemodialysis too quickly?	Disequilibrium syndrome
What are the symptoms of disequilibrium syndrome?	Change in LOC, nausea, vomiting, headache, and twitching.

HEMOPHILIA

Hemophilia is a _____disorder.	Bleeding
Hemophilia A is a deficiency of Factor #_____	VIII
During an acute bleeding episode, you should apply _____ for 15 minutes and apply _____.	Pressure, ice
The inheritance pattern for hemophilia is:	Sex-linked recessive
In hemophilia, the PTT is (up/down); the coagulation or clotting time is (up/down); and the platelet count is (up/down).	Up (increased or longer); up (increased or longer; Neither (hemophilia does not affect platelets)
What does hemarthrosis mean?	Bleeding into the joints.
During bleeding into the joints, you should (mobilize/immobilize) the extremity.	Immobilize to prevent dislodging the clots that do form.
To treat hemarthrosis you should _____ the extremity above the _____.	Elevate, heart
What is the name of frozen factor VIII given to hemophiliacs?	Cryoprecipitate
Once you have stopped the bleeding into the joint how long should the patient wait before bearing weight or doing range of motion?	48 hours

What drug can you apply topically to stop bleeding?	Cryoprecipitate
Which of these symptoms are **not** seen in hemophilia? Prolonged bleeding, petechiae, ecchymosis, or hematoma?	Petechiae

HEPATITIS

Hepatitis is an _____, _____ disease of the _____.	Acute, inflammatory, liver
Hepatitis A, B, C and D are all (bacterial/viral) diseases.	Viral
An early sign of hepatitis A is _____.	Anorexia or fatigue
Early-stage hepatitis often looks like _____.	Flu
In later stages of hepatitis, the ___ turns dark.	Urine
What does pre-icteric mean?	The stage before the patient exhibits jaundice.
What is the icteric stage?	When the patient exhibits jaundice.
What skin symptoms do you see in hepatitis? (Give 2)	Pruritis (itching), jaundice (Both are due to bilirubin accumulation).
Which disease has more severe symptoms-- Hepatitis A or B?	Hepatitis B
Patients with hepatitis have an aversion to _____.	Cigarettes
In hepatitis the _____ are light colored.	Stools: remember the urine is dark and stools are light. (Bilirubin ends up in the skin and urine instead of the stool where it should have gone.)
Is Hepatitis A immunization given before or after exposure?	Hepatitis A immunization is given AFTER an exposure (prophylaxis, 1 shot) or given before as two shots six months apart after age 12 months.

Is Hepatitis B vaccine given before or after exposure?	Hepatitis B vaccine is given BEFORE exposure (in 3 separate doses).

Hepatitis A	Hepatitis B	Hepatitis C
Enteric precautions • Fecal/oral route of transmission • Incubates 3 to 5 weeks • Vaccine available. Can give immune globulin after exposure. • HAsAg- (this is what the blood tests show) Hepatitis A surface Antigen	Watch those needles • HBsAg- (this is what blood tests show) Hepatitis B surface Antigen • HBIG--vaccine • Vaccination available, can give immune globulin after exposure • Transmitted by blood and body fluids • Incubates 5 to 35 weeks	• Watch those needles • Incubates 2 to 23 weeks • Transmitted by blood only • No vaccine, immune globulin doesn't work

HERPES ZOSTER

What is the common name for Herpes Zoster?	Shingles
What type of rash occurs with shingles?	A vesicular rash over the pathway of a sensory nerve.
How long does it take for shingles to heal?	30 days
Who is most at risk of getting shingles?	People who have ever had chickenpox.
What is the most common subjective symptom of shingles?	Pain, pain, pain
What three drugs are given for shingles?	Acyclovir (anti-infective); Tegretol (Anticonvulsant--given to stabilize nerve cell membranes); steroids (anti-inflammatory)
What other disease is related to shingles?	Chickenpox
What organism causes shingles?	Varicella--herpes zoster
What is the #1 nursing diagnosis with shingles?	Alteration in comfort: pain; #2 Impaired skin integrity.

What vaccine prevents shingles?	Zostavax/Shingrix
Zostavax stronger or weaker than the Varicella chicken pox vaccination?	Stronger
Who should get Zostavax/Shingrix?	Patients over 60 years of age who are not immuno suppressed.
How long does Zostavax last?	Longer than 6 years.
What is disseminated herpes zoster?	It is when the virus is in your lungs, circulation, and other organs other than the skin.

HYPERTENSION

Hypertension is an _____ or sustained elevation in the (systolic/diastolic) _____.	Intermittent, diastolic blood pressure.
Hypertension is often fatal if untreated. (T/F)	TRUE
Hypertension is often common in African Americans or Anglo Americans?	African Americans
Aging decreases the risk of hypertension (T/F).	False, it increases the risk.
Obesity increases the risk of (T/F) hypertension.	TRUE
Oral contraceptives (increase/decrease/do not affect) the blood pressure.	Increase
What four organs does hypertension affect most?	Brain (stroke), eyes (blindness), heart (MI), kidney (renal failure).
How many measurements must be made before you can say a person has hypertension?	At least three.
What blood pressure is considered to be hypertension?	Anything greater than 140/90 mm Hg
Which pressure is most damaging, an increased (systolic/diastolic)?	An increased diastolic.

Physiological Adaptation

When a doctor takes three different blood pressure readings at different times, how far apart must the measurements be made?	At least one week.
Can hypertension be cured?	No, just treated.
What class of drug is used first to treat hypertension?	Diuretics
Name the two most common dietary prescriptions used to treat hypertension.	Calorie reduction for weight loss, and sodium restriction.
What two non-dietary lifestyle changes are used commonly to treat hypertension?	Decrease stress, increase activity.
When you take the blood pressure of the client with hypertension you would measure _____ _____, with the client ____, ____ and ____.	Both arms; lying, sitting, and standing.
What do caffeine and smoking do to blood pressure?	Increase it.
What is the #1 side effect of antihypertensives?	Orthostatic hypotension (means you feel weak when you rise to a standing position, because your blood pressure falls).
Would vasodilators or vasoconstrictors treat hypertension?	Vasodilators (decreases resistance)
Would sympathetic stimulators or sympathetic blockers treat hypertension?	Sympathetic blockers (decrease cardiac output and decrease resistance).

HYPOVOLEMIC SHOCK

In hypovolemic shock there is a _____ in the circulating _____ volume--this _____ tissue perfusion with _____.	Decrease; blood; decreases; oxygen
What gauge catheter would you use to start an IV in hypovolemic shock?	16 or larger

191

What is the #1 cause of hypovolemic shock? _____ _____ _____.	Acute blood loss.
What happens to the blood pressure in hypovolemic shock?	It decreases.
What happens to the pulse pressure in hypovolemic shock?	It narrows (becomes a smaller number).
How do you calculate the pulse pressure?	You subtract the diastolic from systolic.
If J. Doe's blood pressure is 100/60, what is his pulse pressure?	40 (100 minus 60 equals 40)
What is the normal pulse pressure?	40 (+ or - 10)
In hypovolemic shock the level of consciousness (LOC) is (increased/decreased).	Decreased
Which heart rate is associated with hypovolemic shock, bradycardia, or tachycardia?	Tachycardia
In hypovolemic shock the output of urine will be less than _____ mL per hour.	25 to 30 mL
The client's skin will be _____, _____, and _____.	Cool, pale, clammy (due to arterial constriction to shunt blood from skin to vital organs).
Which acid-base disorder is MOST associated with hypovolemic shock?	Metabolic acidosis (due to lactic acid accumulation--no oxygen=anaerobic metabolism).
Of all the following, which one(s) increase in hypovolemic shock? Blood pressure, output, heart rate, pH, LOC, pulse pressure, respiratory rate?	Only the heart rate and respiratory rate.
What does compensated shock mean?	It means that the tachycardia is keeping blood pressure high enough to perfuse the organs.
What are the first two signs of hypovolemic shock?	Change in LOC and tachycardia.

What is the #1 medical treatment of hypovolemic shock?	Replace blood and fluids
What are mast trousers?	Pneumatic device placed around the legs and lower body that is inflated to force blood centrally.
Do clients in hypovolemic shock have to have a Foley inserted?	Yes, to measure urine output (when output is >30 mL per hour the shock has resolved).
In what position would you place a client in suspected hypovolemic shock?	On the back with arms and legs elevated.
How often are vital signs measured in hypovolemic shock?	Every 15 minutes
If the blood pressure (systolic) falls below 80 mm Hg, what would you do first in hypovolemic shock?	Increase the oxygen flow rate.

IDIOPATHIC THROMBOCYTOPENIC PURPURA—ITP

What is idiopathic thrombocytopenia purpura?	It is a blood disease in which there is a severe decrease in platelets (unknown reason).
What is the speculated cause of ITP?	Autoimmune
What two things do the clients with ITP complain of before clinical diagnosis?	Bleeding gums and epistaxis (nosebleed).
What two observable skin signs are common with ITP?	Ecchymosis, bruises, petechiae (small dot-like hemorrhages).
What organ is enlarged with ITP?	The spleen.
Why is this organ removed in ITP?	The spleen destroys old platelets, so if you remove the organ that destroys platelets, you increase your platelet count.
What lab value is most decreased in ITP?	Platelet count

Because these clients are on steroids, they have an increased risk of....	Infection (fungal & viral primarily)
Transfusions with what product are common in ITP?	Platelets
What is the most life-threatening complication of ITP?	Hemorrhage
Name the class of drugs most given to clients with ITP?	Steroids (decadron, prednisone, hexadrolsolucortef); Immunosuppressive agents (immuran)

INFECTIOUS MONONUCLEOSIS

What body system is attacked by mononucleosis?	Lymphatic
What blood count will be elevated in mononucleosis?	Lymphocytes increase, monocytes increase, granulocytes decrease.
How long is the average recovery from mononucleosis?	Three weeks
What two medications are given to clients with mononucleosis?	ASA--steroids if a bad case.
What organism causes mononucleosis?	Epstein-Barr herpes virus
Give four symptoms of mononucleosis.	Sore throat, malaise, stiff neck (nuchal rigidity), and nausea.
Give three nursing measures for care of clients with mononucleosis.	Rest, ASA, fluids
What age group most commonly gets mononucleosis?	15 to 35
What organ should **not** be palpated in the client with mononucleosis?	The spleen, it could rupture which may lead to shock and death.
How is mononucleosis transmitted?	Respiratory droplets

Upon physical exam of a client with mononucleosis, you find	Increased temperature, enlarged lymph nodes, splenomegaly.
Name two complications of mononucleosis.	Hepatitis, ruptured spleen, meningoencephalitis

INTUSSUSCEPTION

Intussusception is a condition in which the bowel _____ into itself.	Telescopes
Intussusception is more common in (boys/girls).	Boys
Name two ways to correct intussusception.	Barium enema (the barium pushes the bowel straight), or surgical repair.
The major complication of intussusception is _____ of the bowel.	Necrosis
Intussusception occurs most commonly at age _____ months.	6
Intussusception is commonly seen in children who have _____ _____.	Cystic fibrosis
Describe the cry of the infant with intussusception.	Piercing cry
In addition to experiencing severe abdominal Pain, what position the infant will assume.	Pull legs up to chest/abdomen
Describe the stool of a child with intussusception.	Currant-jelly stool, bloody mucous. If surgery is scheduled and the infant has a normal bowel movement, surgery may be canceled. Call HCP.
Describe the vomitus of a child with intussusception.	Bile stained

KIDNEY STONES AND THE DIET

What is the primary dietary prescription for calcium nephrolithiasis?	Low calcium diet
For the client with calcium nephrolithiasis the diet should be _____ ash.	Acid

If the kidney stone is calcium phosphate the diet must be low in _____ too.	Phosphorus
The primary diet treatment for uric acid nephrolithiasis is _____ _____.	Low purine
The client with uric acid nephrolithiasis should have a diet low in _____.	Methionine
What is methionine?	The precursor of the amino acid cystine (precursor=material out of which something is made).
Name two foods high in methionine.	Milk, eggs
Clients with cystine nephrolithiasis should have a(n) _____ ash diet.	Alkaline
Increasing fluids to over 3000 cc per day is more effective in treating renal calculi (kidney stones) than <u>any</u> dietary modification. (T/F?)	True. It's more important to flush the urinary tract than worry about what you're eating.

LARYNGOTRACHEOBRONCHITIS—LTB

What is the common name for LTB?	Croup
What is the typical temperature elevation in croup?	Low grade, usually below 102°, but can go up to 104°.
Are antibiotics helpful for croup? For epiglottitis?	For croup, no. For epiglottitis, yes.
Is croup viral or bacterial?	Viral
With which condition is croup most often confused?	Epiglottitis
Can croup be managed at home? Can epiglottitis be managed at home?	Yes No, epiglottitis is a medical emergency.
Are sedatives used for children with croup?	No, because this would mask the signs of respiratory distress.
What causes epiglottitis? A virus or bacteria?	H. influenza bacteria

What is the best treatment for croup?	Cool moist air
What should never be done to a child with epiglottitis?	Never put anything in the child's mouth, ie, a tongue blade can lead to obstruction.
What are the typical signs and symptoms of croup?	Barking cough, inspiratory stridor, labored respiratory pattern.
What three signs tell you that the child has epiglottitis instead of croup?	Muffled voice, drooling, increased fever
When is croup bad enough to be evaluated by a doctor?	When retractions, and high-pitched stridor are present.

LEUKEMIA

Leukemia is cancer of the _____-forming tissues.	Blood
The type of cell that is most common and problematic in leukemia is _____.	Immature WBC
In leukemia the RBC count is (high/low).	Low, because the bone marrow is going "wild" producing all those immature WBCs-- no energy or nutrients left over to make RBCs.
In leukemia, the platelet count is (high/low).	Low, because the bone marrow is going "wild" producing all those immature WBCs -no energy or nutrients to make platelets.
Because the RBCs are low, the patient will exhibit _____ and _____.	Pallor and fatigue
Because of the immature WBCs, the patient is at risk for _____.	Infection
Because of low platelets, the patient is at risk for _____, _____, and _____.	Bruising, ecchymosis, bleeding, petechiae
What causes lymph gland enlargement in leukemia?	All those small immature WBCs clog the lymphatic system.

Should you take a rectal temperature on a child with leukemia?	No
Should you take an oral temperature on a child with leukemia?	Yes, as long as they are over four years old, in remission, and have no sores in their mouth.
Should the child with active leukemia use straws, forks, cups?	NO straws, NO forks, YES, they can use cups
The nurse's priority in treating a child with newly diagnosed leukemia is	Decreasing risk of infection
When the leukemia child's platelets and WBCs are low, his activities should be....	Limited
When the platelet and WBCs are low the nurse should not insert a	Suppository
Are IM injections and IV sticks permitted on a child with leukemia?	When the platelets and WBCs are low, IMs are to be avoided; IV sticks are to be limited, and only done when absolutely necessary (i.e., to give chemotherapy or measure blood counts).
Why are children on chemotherapy also on Zyloprim (Allopurinol)?	To prevent uric acid kidney stones (Remember when chemotherapy kills cancer cells, purines and uric acid build up and could cause kidney stones).
Why do some children with leukemia have joint pain?	The immature WBCs infiltrate the joint and cause inflammation.
Why is a child with leukemia at risk for neurological symptoms due to increased intracranial pressure?	The immature WBCs infiltrate the brain and cause inflammation.
What is alopecia?	Hair loss
If the platelet count is low what drug should the child not take?	Aspirin

Is the alopecia of chemotherapy permanent?	NO, it will grow back (remember, the alopecia of radiation therapy is permanent because the follicle is destroyed too).
What does "ANC" stand for?	Absolute Neutrophil Count
What is the ANC used for in leukemia?	If the ANC is below 500, then the patient will be in protective isolation.
Which is used more commonly to decide if the patient should be in isolation: the WBC or the ANC?	The ANC is more reliable and valid.

MASTOIDITIS

What is mastoiditis?	Inflammation/infection of the mastoid process
What is the most common cause of mastoiditis?	Chronic otitis media
What are the 4 signs and symptoms of mastoiditis?	Drainage from ear, high fever, headache and ear pain, tenderness over mastoid process.
What unusual post-operative complication can result from mastoidectomy?	Facial nerve paralysis due to accidental damage during surgery (lawsuit time!)
What should you do to assess facial nerve paralysis post-mastoidectomy?	Have the patient smile and wrinkle forehead.
What is the medical treatment of mastoiditis?	Systemic antibiotics
What is the surgery for mastoiditis called?	Simple or radical mastoidectomy
Will a simple mastoidectomy worsen hearing?	No, a radical mastoidectomy may.
Should the nurse change the post mastoidectomy dressing?	No, reinforce it. Physician changes first post-op dressing.
What is a common side effect of mastoidectomy?	Dizziness (vertigo)
What is a major nursing diagnosis post mastoidectomy?	Safety

MENIERE'S DISEASE

Define Meniere's Disease.	An increase in endolymph in the inner ear, causing severe vertigo.
What is the famous triad of symptoms in Meniere's?	Paroxysmal whirling vertigo--sensorineural hearing loss--tinnitus (ringing in the ears).
Does Meniere's occur more in men or women?	Women
What should the client do if they get an attack?	Bed rest
What safety measures should be followed with Meniere's?	Side rails up x4, ambulate only with assistance.
What age group in Meniere's highest in?	40 to 60
What can PREVENT the attacks of Meniere's?	Avoid sudden movements.
What electrolyte is given to people with Meniere's?	Ammonium chloride
What is the surgery done for Meniere's?	Labyrinthectomy
What disease often follows labyrinthectomy?	Bell's palsy--facial paralysis, will go away in a few months.
What is the activity order after labyrinthectomy?	Bed rest
When surgery is performed for Meniere's, what are the consequences?	Hearing is totally lost in the surgical ear.
What should the client avoid after labyrinthectomy?	Sudden movements and increased Na foods.
What type of diet is the client with Meniere's on?	Low salt
What two classes of drugs are given in Meniere's?	Antihistamines and diuretics like Acetazolamide (Diamox)

MENINGITIS

Meningitis is an inflammation of the _____ of the _____ and spinal _____.	Linings, brain, cord
Meningitis can be caused by _____, _____, and _____.	Viruses, bacteria, chemicals
The four most common organisms that cause meningitis are...	Pneumococcus, meningococcus, streptococcus, H. influenza
The child with meningitis is most likely to be (lethargic/irritable) at first.	Irritable
What visual symptom will the patient with meningitis have?	Photophobia (over-sensitivity to light)
What is the most common Musculo-skeletal symptom of meningitis?	Stiff neck-nuchal rigidity
Will the patient with meningitis have a headache?	Yes
Kernig's sign is positive when there is pain in the _____ when attempting to straighten the leg with the _____ flexed.	Knee; hip
What type of vomiting is present in meningitis?	Projectile
What is the definitive diagnostic test for meningitis?	Lumbar puncture with culture of CSF (cerebro-spinal fluid)
If the patient has meningitis, the CSF shows _____ pressure, _____ WBC, _____ protein, _____ glucose.	Increased, increased, increased, decreased
On what type of isolation will the patient with meningitis be?	Contact and respiratory droplet precautions
How long will the patient with meningitis be on these precautions?	Until they have been on an antibiotic for 48 hours.
The room of a patient with meningitis should be _____ and _____.	Dark and quiet

The client with meningitis can develop _____.	Seizures
What is opisthotonos?	Arching of back (entire body) from hyperextension of the neck and ankles, due to severe meningeal irritation.
If a patient has opisthotonos, in what position would you place them?	Side-lying

MIGRAINE HEADACHE

What type of environmental modification is best for a migraine?	Dark, quiet, environment
The long-term treatment of migraine focuses upon....	Assessing things that bring on stress and then planning to avoid them.
What type of pain is typical of migraines?	Throbbing
Are migraines more or less common in men?	Less
Besides pain, people with migraines complain of what other symptoms?	Nausea and vomiting, and visual disturbances.
What are the processes occurring in migraines?	Reflex constriction then dilation of cerebral arteries.
Where is the pain of migraine most likely located?	Temporal, supraorbital
Name a drug given to treat migraine?	Sansert (methsergide), Cafergot (Prophylaxis: Imipramine)
Are migraine headaches usually unilateral or bilateral?	Unilateral
When Inderal (propranolol) is given in migraine headache, is it used to <u>prevent</u> or <u>treat</u> an attack?	To prevent. It does not treat.

MULTIPLE SCLEROSIS—MS

MS is a progressive _____ disease of the CNS.	Demyelinating

Myelin promotes _____, _____ _____ of nerve impulses.	Fast, smooth conduction
With demyelination the nerve impulses become _____ and _____.	Slow, uncoordinated
MS affects men more than women. (T/F)	FALSE
What age group usually gets MS?	20 to 40
MS usually occurs in (hot/cool) climates.	Cool
What is the first sign of MS?	Blurred or double vision
MS can lead to urinary incontinence. (T/F)	TRUE
MS can lead to impotence in males. (T/F)	TRUE
Patients with MS should be taught to walk with a _____ - _____ gait.	Wide-based
Why are Adrenocorticotropic Hormone (ACTH) and prednisone given during acute MS?	To decrease edema in the demyelination process.
For acute exacerbations of MS _____ per IV is often used.	ACTH (Corticotropin)
What drug can be given to treat urinary retention in MS?	Urecholine, Bethanocol
Will the muscles of MS clients be spastic or flaccid?	Spastic
What three drugs can be given for muscle spasms?	Diazepam (Valium), Baclofen (Lioresal), Dantrium (Dantrolene)
Baclofen causes (constipation/diarrhea).	Constipation
Dantrium causes (constipation/diarrhea).	Diarrhea (hint: the D's go together, Dantrium and Diarrhea).
Patients with MS should have fluids (forced/restricted?)	Forced

The diet of a patient with MS should be _____-ash.	Acid
What major sense is affected most in MS (besides vision)?	Tactile (touch)--they burn themselves easily.
Which will bring on a MS exacerbation: over-heating or chilling?	Both will; but they tend to do better in cool weather (summer will always be a bad time for MS patients).

MYASTHENIA GRAVIS

In Myasthenia Gravis (MG) there is a disturbance in transmission of impulses at the _____ _____.	Neuromuscular junction
The #1 sign of MG is _____ ____ _____.	Severe muscle weakness
What is the unique adjective given to describe the early signs of MG?	The early signs (difficulty swallowing, visual problems) are referred to as BULBAR signs.
MG affects men more than women. (T/F)	False, affects women more than men.
When women get MG, they are usually old or young?	Young
When men get MG, they are usually old or young?	Old
What neurotransmitter is problematic in MG?	Acetylcholine
What class of drug is used to treat MG?	Anticholinesterases
What ending do anticholinesterases have?	--stigmine
Are anticholinesterases sympathetic or parasympathetic?	Parasympathetic
Anticholinesterases will have (sympathetic/cholinergic) side effects.	Cholinergic (they will mimic the parasympathetic nervous system).
What surgery CAN be done for MG?	Thymectomy (removal of thymus)
The severe muscle weakness of MG gets better with exercise. (T/F)	False, it is worse with activity.

What will the facial appearance of a patient with MG look like?	Mask-like with a snarling smile (called a mysathenic smile)
If a patient has MG, what will be the results of the Tensilon Test?	The patient will show a dramatic sudden increase in muscle strength.
Besides the Tensilon Test, what other diagnostic tests confirm a diagnosis of MG?	Electromyogram (EMG)
What is the most important thing to remember about giving Mestinon and other anticholinesterases?	They must be given EXACTLY ON TIME; at home, they might need to set their alarm.
Do you give anticholinesterases with or without food?	With food, about ½ hour ac; giving ac helps strengthen muscles of swallowing.
What type of diet should the patient with MG be on?	Soft
What equipment should be at the bedside of an MG patient?	Suction apparatus (for meals), Tracheostomy/ endotube (for ventilation)
Name the two types of crises that a MG patient can have.	Cholinergic (too much Pyridostigmine (Mestinon) Myasthenic (not enough Mestinon)
The #1 danger in both Myasthenic and Cholinergic crisis is _____ _____.	Respiratory arrest

MYOCARDIAL INFARCTION—MI

What words will the client use to describe the pain of an MI?	Crushing, heavy, squeezing, radiating to the left arm, neck, jaw, shoulder.
What is an MI?	Severe chest pain unrelieved by rest and nitroglycerine.
What's the #1 symptom of an MI?	Either a clot, spasm or plaque that blocks the coronary arteries causing loss of blood supply to the heart and myocardial cell death.
Males are more likely to get an MI than females. (T/F)	TRUE

Death due to MI occurs within _____ of symptom onset in 50% of all patients.	One hour
What pain medication is given for the pain of a MI? (Give two)	Morphine, Nitroglycerine
What is the reason for giving post MI patients ASA?	To prevent platelets from forming clots in the coronary arteries.
Name a new drug with anti-platelet activity.	Clopidogrel (Plavix), Eliquis (Apixaban)
The three most common complications after MI are _____ _____, _____, and _____.	Cardiogenic shock, arrhythmia, CHF
Give another name for a MI.	Heart attack
What will the activity order be for the post-MI client?	Bed rest with bedside commode.
What is the most common arrhythmia after a MI?	Premature ventricular contractions (PVCs)
What cardiac enzymes indicate an MI?	Elevated CPK, LDH, SGOT
What serum protein rises soonest after myocardial cell injury?	Troponin
Do people without cell damage have troponin in their blood?	No, it is only present when myocardial cells are damaged.
How soon after cell damage does troponin increase?	As soon as 3 hours (can remain elevated for 7 days).
When will the client with an MI be allowed to engage in sexual intercourse after an MI?	6 weeks after discharge
Will fluid resuscitation (administering large amounts of IV fluid) treat cardiogenic shock?	No, you must use cardiac drugs (giving IV's and blood will not help this kind of shock).
Will the client with a MI be nauseated? ...diaphoretic?	Yes Yes
What will the extremities of the client with a MI feel like?	Cold, Clammy

What is the permanent EKG change seen post MI?	ST wave changes
Of CPK and LDH which rises earliest?	CPK
What drug will be used to treat PVCs of MI?	Lidocaine
Will the client with a MI need 100% O2 for their entire stay in the hospital?	No, just moderate flow (42% or 3 to 6 liters for the first 48 hours).

NEPHROTIC SYNDROME

Is nephrotic syndrome a disease?	No, it is not a specific disease, it is a group of symptoms that can result from many diseases.
Is there any hematuria in nephrosis?	No, there is no hematuria in the -oses, but there is hematuria in the -itis's.
What are the dietary modifications for nephrosis?	High carbohydrates, moderate protein, low sodium
What is the #1 nursing diagnosis in nephrosis?	Alteration in fluid volume, excess
What are the two pathophysiologic processes in nephrotic syndrome?	Glomerular inflammation, loss of protein
What symptom is MOST common in nephrosis?	Generalized severe edema
What 2 classes of drugs are given for nephrosis?	Steroids, diuretics
Is bed rest common in treating nephrosis?	It is occasionally done, but not nearly as common as in acute glomerulo-nephritis, it usually is most appropriate when edema is severe.
In nephrotic syndrome, the blood pressure will be most likely (hypotensive/hypertensive)?	Hypotensive: remember in acute glomerulonephritis, the blood pressure is hypertensive.
In nephrotic syndrome, the urine is (frothy/very dark or tea-colored)?	Frothy: remember in AGN, it is tea colored.
Is scrotal edema common in nephrosis?	Yes

What is done for scrotal edema?	Elevate the scrotum on a scrotal sling and apply ice.

OSTEOARTHRITIS

Osteoarthritis is a _____ disease of the _____.	Degenerative, joint
Osteoarthritis is most commonly caused by the wear and tear of life. (T/F?)	TRUE
The most common symptom of osteoarthritis is_____ _____.	Joint Pain
What two joints are most commonly affected in osteoarthritis?	Knee and hip
To control the pain of osteoarthritis one should use heat or cold?	Heat
What three medications are used in osteoarthritis?	Aspirin, non-steroidal anti-inflammatory (Indocin, Ibuprofen), steroids
What do you observe on the fingers of the client with osteoarthritis?	Heberden's nodes
Are Heberden's nodes painful?	Not in the beginning, can be later as swelling occurs.
Are rest periods and range of motion exercises appropriate in the care of osteoarthritis?	Yes, rest is probably the most effective thing they can do.
The pain of osteoarthritis is usually better or worse with rest? With activity?	Better with rest, worse with activity
What age group gets osteoarthritis?	60–80-year-olds
Osteoarthritis is more common in females. (T/F?)	False, it occurs with equal frequency.
For cervical osteoarthritis the client should wear...	A cervical collar

What is arthroplasty?	Joint replacement
What is arthrodesis?	Joint fusion

OTOSCLEROSIS

What is otosclerosis?	Overgrowth of spongy bone in the middle ear that doesn't allow the bones of the middle ear to vibrate.
What will the client with otosclerosis complain of besides hearing loss?	Buzzing or ringing in the ears (tinnitus)
Do people have a loss of hearing with this?	Yes
What is a corrective surgery for otosclerosis called?	Stapedectomy
Should side rails be up after stapedectomy?	Yes, clients may feel dizzy.
What should the client avoid post stapedectomy?	Coughing, sneezing, blowing nose, swimming, showers, flying
What warning should you give the client about getting up after stapedectomy?	Get up slowly
What should the client expect regarding hearing post-stapedectomy?	An initial decrease with the benefits of surgery noticeable in 6 weeks.
What should the client do if he must sneeze?	Open his mouth, this de-pressurizes the middle ear.
What type of hearing loss is associated with otosclerosis?	Conductive
Which sex has a higher incidence of otosclerosis?	Women
Do hearing aids help hearing in otosclerosis?	Yes
What will be the results of the Rinne test in otosclerosis?	Bone conduction will be better than air conduction.

Is stapedectomy done under general or local anesthesia?	Local
If the client complains of decreased hearing after stapedectomy, what would you say?	It is normal due to edema. The hearing will start to improve within six weeks.
Which side will the client be allowed to lie upon post-stapedectomy?	Depends on MD: operative side promotes drainage; un-operative side prevents graft dislodgement. Don't make a big deal of position post-op.
What two drugs are commonly given post-stapedectomy?	Codeine/Demerol for pain, Dramamine for dizziness

OVARIAN CYSTS

Cysts on the ovaries are usually malignant. (T/F?)	False, usually benign.
What is the #1 reason why HCP's remove ovarian cysts?	Remove before they transform into malignant.
Do small ovarian cysts cause symptoms?	No, only large ones.
Common signs of large ovarian cysts are...	Low back pain, pelvic pain, abnormal bleeding
What does torsion of an ovarian cyst mean?	Twisting of cyst with interruption of its blood supply.
What is the big danger from torsion?	Necrosis and rupture of ovary
What other disorders resemble rupture of ovarian cysts?	Appendicitis, rupture of a fallopian tube pregnancy.
What effect do oral contraceptives have on ovarian cysts?	They cause it to stop growing and decrease in size.
What are the 3 most common signs of ovarian cyst rupture?	Pain, abdominal distention, abdominal rigidity
Compare signs of non-ruptured ovarian cysts with the signs of a ruptured ovarian cyst. (Give 3 for each)	Non-ruptured: low back pain, dull pelvic pain, abnormal uterine bleeding especially with menstruation Ruptured: acute pain, abdominal distention, and abdominal rigidity

After surgery to remove an ovarian cyst, the woman can return to normal activities between _____ to _____ weeks.	4-6 weeks
How soon after removal of an ovarian cyst can a woman resume sexual intercourse?	4-6 weeks
Should a woman douche after surgery to remove an ovarian cyst?	No, it is not good to douche on a regular basis, it destroys natural protective vaginal flora.

PACEMAKERS AND TELEMETRY

Pacemakers are _____ devices designed to give the _____ _____ impulses to regulate the rhythm of the heat	Electronic Myocardial muscle
Can pacemakers be temporary?	Yes.
Can pacemakers be permanent?	Yes.
Pacemakers are primarily used for _____ and conduction disorders like _____ _____ and heart _____.	Bradycardia A Fib Blocks
Can pacemakers be used to evaluate cardiac function in advanced CHF?	Yes. But both ventricles would need wiring for that.
What is the big difference between temporary and permanent pacemakers?	With **Temporary** pacemakers the generator/controller devices are OUTSIDE the body and only the wiring is internal, Whereas, with **Permanent** pacemakers the generator/controller devices are implanted under the skin on the chest wall, so everything is internal.
How long can a permanent pacemaker battery last	Up to 12 years but most likely 10.
In the first 24 hours after pacemaker insertion how often should rhythm strips be recorded?	Every 4 hours.

In the first 24 hours after pacemaker insertion what activity limitation does the patient have to follow?	Do not overextend or overuse the extremity closest to the implant.
How long should the patient avoid showering after pacemaker implantation?	2 weeks
Can the extremity closest to the implant be immobilized for 24 hours post insertion?	Yes
With what will the arm be immobilized?	A sling
What action is most dangerous after pacer insertion?	Raising the arm...it should be avoided for 3 weeks.
Can a patient with a permanent pacemaker swim?	Yes.
When can a patient drive after pacemaker insertion?	In 3 weeks
Telemetry is an _____ device that reads impulses generated by the _____ by means of _____electrode pads and _____ relay box.	Electronic Heart (myocardium) External External
The relay box transmits the electrical; activity of the heart to the _____ _____ at the _____ station.	Monitor bank Nurse's
The BIG difference between pacemakers and telemetry devices is that Pacemakers _____ electrical impulses _____ the myocardium and telemetry devices _____ electrical impulses _____ the myocardium.	Deliver TO Record FROM (Think of telemetry as "Read Only")
Can a patient get shocked or electrocuted by telemetry?	No. It Is read only
Can a patient be on telemetry at home?	Yes, but usually with a Holter monitor.
Can a patient have an EXTERNAL (temporary) pacemaker and telemetry at the same time?	No. but they can have telemetry with a permanent (internal)

Does monitoring telemetry have an additional competency documentation requirement beyond the RN license?	Yes, a nurse must have documented competency before taking on telemetry responsibilities. The institution is responsible for providing such a course.
Should a nurse with no telemetry training care for a patient with telemetry?	No
What diagnostic test is required before a patient is placed on telemetry?	A baseline 12 lead EKG.
What are two major actions a nurse can take to obtain high quality telemetry readings?	Proper placement of electrode leads AND good contact between patch and skin.
Can parts of the chest be shaved to get good electrode patch contact with the skin?	Yes
Can a person on telemetry shower.	Yes, but the leads need to be removed and the box removed. (Replaced once finished).
Can a patient on telemetry leave the unit/floor?	Yes, but the transmitter box needs to go with them and the monitor reader on the unit needs to be turned off with a note that the patient is "off unit".
The right arm lead is placed where?	Under right midclavicle.
The right arm lead is what color?	White. Think "white on right"
The left arm lead is placed where?	Under the left midclavicle.
What color is the left arm lead?	Black
Where is the left leg lead placed?	Below the left rib cage on abdomen in midclavicular line
What color is the left leg lead?	Red. (for the left side leads think …… "Smoke over fire") that is black (smoke) over red (fire).
IF there is a right leg lead, where is it? What color is it?	The right leg lead is in the same spot as the left leg lead except on the right side. It is green.
If a nurse is not getting a reading from a telemetry device, what should they do first?	Check leads then Replace the batteries!!!

PARKINSON'S DISEASE

What structures in the brain are most affected in Parkinson's?	Basal ganglia
The neurotransmitter imbalance that causes Parkinson's is a _____ in _____ _____.	Decrease, dopamine activity
What drugs can cause a Parkinson-like syndrome?	Haloperidal, (Haldol), major tranquilizers-- drugs that end in "-azine"
What is the classic motor manifestation of Parkinson's?	Pill-rolling and tremors
What type of rigidity is typical of Parkinson's?	Cogwheel
Parkinson's patients move fast or slow?	Slow
What type of gait is seen in Parkinson's?	Shuffling slow gait
Patients with Parkinson's have_____ speech.	Monotone
Patients with Parkinson's tend to have constipation or diarrhea?	Constipation
Name four drugs used to treat Parkinson's.	Levodopa, Sinement, Symmetrol, Cogentin, Artane, Parlodel
In what chair should Parkinson's patients sit?	Firm, hard backed
What time of day can be particularly dangerous for the Parkinson's patient?	Mealtime, due to choking
When a patient is taking Levodopa, he should have assistance getting out of bed because...	Of orthostatic hypotension
What vitamin should patients on Levodopa avoid?	B6, pyridoxine
Levodopa should be given with or without food?	With
What might Levodopa do to patients' urine?	Make it very dark
The tremors of Parkinson's will get better or worse when they purposefully move or perform a task?	Better, they tremor more when not performing an action.

PEDICULOSIS

What is the common name for pediculosis?	Lice
What is a common finding with pediculosis pubis?	Reddish-brown dust in the underwear
What common household solution is used to remove nits?	Vinegar. Nits are the eggs of lice that adhere to the hair shaft.
What shampoo is used for lice?	Hyoscine hydrochloride (Kwell)
Where are head lice most found?	At the back of the head and behind the ears.
On what do lice feed?	Blood
After treatment, how long do you have to inspect for lice?	Inspect for 2 weeks to be sure that they are all gone.
What is the most common symptom of lice?	Itching
What is the most dangerous toxicity of Kwell?	CNS toxicity

PEMPHIGUS

What is typical of the lesions of pemphigus?	Foul-smelling, blisters break easily, seen in the elderly, cause unknown
What is the characteristic lesion of pemphigus?	Large vesicular bullae
What are bullae?	Large blisters
What chemical is added to the bath water of a client with pemphigus?	Potassium permanganate
What precaution must be taken with potassium permanganate?	Be careful that no undissolved crystals touch the client; it will burn the skin.
What is the typical skin care of pemphigus?	Cool wet dressings
What unusual nursing diagnosis is high priority in pemphigus?	Alteration in fluid and electrolyte balance
What are the top three nursing interventions in pemphigus?	Oral care, protection from infection, encouraging high fluid intake

What kinds of fluids will clients with pemphigus drink best?	Cold fluids
What drugs are most commonly used?	Steroids
Should steroids be given with meals?	Always
What is the #1 cause of death in pemphigus?	Overwhelming infection

Definition: An acute or chronic disease of adults, characterized by occurrence of successive crops of bullae that appear suddenly on apparently normal skin and disappear, leaving pigmented spots. It may be attended by itching and burning and constitutional disturbance. The disease, if untreated, is usually fatal.

A characteristic finding is a positive Nikolsky sign: When pressure is applied tangential to the surface of affected skin, the outer layer of epidermis will detach from the lower layer. (Probably autoimmune)

PERITONEAL DIALYSIS

Define peritoneal dialysis. (PD)	The removal of wastes, electrolytes and fluids from the body using the peritoneum as a dialyzing membrane.
When PD is being used the client must be on heparin. (T/F?)	False, you do not need to be heparinized for peritoneal, but you do need to be heparinized for hemodialysis.
How long does one episode/course of PD last?	Could be 10 hours
With PD there is a high/low risk of peritonitis?	High
When fluid accumulates in the abdomen during PD what problem does the client experience first?	Dyspnea - SOB or difficulty breathing, due to the inability of the diaphragm to descend.
What nutrient is lost in the highest amounts during PD?	Protein
Can a client who had recent bowel surgery get PD?	No
Should a client who is having breathing problems receive PD?	No

What body surface must be punctured to administer PD?	The abdomen
The solution introduced into the peritoneum during PD is called ...	Dialysate
Before allowing the dialysate to flow into the peritoneal cavity it must be _____ to _____ temperature.	Warmed, body
Before PD it is important the client be...	Weighed, to assess water loss or gain.
What force is used to introduce the dialysate into the peritoneum?	Gravity only, no pumps
How fast does the dialysate usually flow into the peritoneum?	In 10 minutes
How long is the dialysate allowed to remain in the peritoneum before it is drained out?	15-30 minutes
How long does it usually take for the dialysate to drain out of the peritoneum?	10 minutes: (10 minutes flow in, 30 minutes in abdominal cavity, 10 minutes flow out = total of 50 minutes)
If the dialysate does not drain out well, you would first?	Have them turn side to side.
What color is the dialysate when it comes out?	Straw colored - clear
Should you raise the HOB to increase drainage of the dialysate?	Yes
How often do you measure vital signs during PD?	Every 15 minutes during the first cycle and every hour thereafter.
Can a client on PD: Sit in a chair? Eat? Urinate? Defecate?	Yes, to all.
If too much fluid is removed during PD, the client will experience...	Decreased blood pressure (hypotension)

If the client absorbs too much of the dialysate the client will experience...	Increased blood pressure (circulatory overload)
If the client complains of dyspnea during PD you would first _____, then _____.	Slow the flow, elevate HOB
If the client complains of abdominal pain during PD, you would first...	Encourage them to move about
Cloudy drainage in the dialysate most commonly means...	Peritonitis, (Not good, call HCP)
What would you do if you noticed a small amount of blood come out in the first few bottles that were infused?	Nothing, this is normal: the blood is due to the initial puncture of the abdomen.
What precautions are important in the care of the client receiving PD?	Safety, because they get dizzy.
Is I&O important to record during PD?	Yes
How high should the dialysate bag be when it's being infused?	Shoulder height

PERNICIOUS ANEMIA

What factor do clients with pernicious anemia lack?	Intrinsic factor. It has no other name.
What vitamin is not absorbed in a patient with pernicious anemia?	Vit B-12
What is another name for Vitamin B-12?	Extrinsic factor.
Why isn't Vitamin B-12 absorbed in pernicious anemia?	Because these patients lack intrinsic factor.
What happens when patients with pernicious anemia don't absorb Vitamin B-12?	Their RBC's do not mature, and they become seriously anemic.

What other disease can be confused with pernicious anemia?	Angina pectoris
What are some classic and unique signs of pernicious anemia?	Beefy red tongue, numbness and tingling of the hands, sores in the mouth, chest pain.
What is the medical treatment for pernicious anemia?	IM injections of Vitamin B-12
How long must the client receive this medical treatment?	For the rest of life
Can we cure pernicious anemia?	No, just treat the symptoms.
What unique urine test is done to diagnose pernicious anemia?	The Schilling test
Is it okay to give B12 orally to a client with pernicious anemia?	No, it will never be absorbed due to a lack of intrinsic factor.
What neurologic test do they do for this anemia?	The Romberg test (a test for balance), in normal people this test is negative, in the client with pernicious anemia this test becomes positive.

PHOTOTHERAPY

What is primary use of phototherapy?	To treat neonatal jaundice.
What chemical causes jaundice in neonates? Why?	Excess bilirubin. Usually due to breakdown of red blood cells.
Why are high bilirubin levels so dangerous to neonates?	Unconjugated bilirubin can cross the blood brain barrier and cause encephalitis.
Phototherapy involves exposing the neonates _____ to a _____-_____ light source that makes the _____ water soluble and thus excreted into the _____.	Skin Blue-green Bilirubin Urine

Phototherapy lights are always set on low intensity to prevent burns to the skin. (T/F?)	False. Phototherapy lights are always set at **highest** intensity. There is no risk for burn.
Can an infant continue to breast feed while on phototherapy?	Yes. Unless the bilirubin is close to 20. Then they can't be out of the phototherapy that long.
What is a name for the phototherapy lights?	Bili-lights
What should a neonate wear and what should a neonate NOT wear when phototherapy is in use?	They must wear opaque goggles/glasses and should not wear any clothing, so the maximum amount of skin is exposed to the lights.
How far away are bili lights from the neonate?	About 5/6 inches!! In other words, as close as possible without a safety concern.

PNEUMONIA

Pneumonia is an _____ in the _____.	Infection, alveoli of lungs
Pneumonia is only caused by bacteria. (T/F?)	False, it can be caused by viruses and aspiration.
Which blood gas disorder is most common in pneumonia?	Respiratory alkalosis because the hyperventilation blows off more CO_2 than the consolidation traps in the blood.
What is Prevner13?	Pneumococcal conjugate vaccine, it is called PCV13. It immunizes against pneumococcal pneumonia.
Who should get PCV13?	People over 60.
What type of immunity does PCV13	Active immunity.
How often do you get PCV13?	Once. IM.
What is the big danger with PCV13?	Anaphylactic shock

POLYCYTHEMIA VERA

What is polycythemia vera?	A blood disease in which there is an increase in erythrocytes, leukocytes, and platelets.
What is the typical complexion of a client with polycythemia vera?	Ruddy red, almost purple
What procedure is done to relieve symptoms in polycythemia vera?	Phlebotomy
What is phlebotomy?	Drain off 200-500 mL of blood from body (opposite of transfusion)
What type of diet will people with polycythemia vera be on?	Low iron
What are the three signs of this disease?	Headache, weakness, itching
Is hemoglobin increased or decreased in this disease?	Increased
What oral problem will people with polycythemia vera have?	Bleeding mucous membranes
What organ will be enlarged in polycythemia vera?	The spleen because it is destroying the excessive RBC's.
Due to increased destruction of RBC's seen in polycythemia vera what blood level will be increased?	Uric acid levels will be high (remember - uric acid levels are always high when cells are being destroyed as in hemolysis, chemotherapy, or radiation therapy).
What drug is most used in polycythemia vera?	Myleran---(this is usually used for bone marrow cancer)

PULMONARY EDEMA

Pulmonary edema is accumulation of _____ in the lung.	Fluid

Pulmonary edema is a common complication of _____ disorders.	Cardiovascular
Pulmonary edema usually results from _____ _____ failure.	Left ventricular
What force causes the pulmonary edema in left ventricular failure?	Increased hydrostatic pressure in the pulmonary capillaries
Can letting IVs run in too fast cause pulmonary edema?	Yes, in the client with poor cardiovascular function.
What are the four classic signs of pulmonary edema?	Dyspnea on exertion, paroxysmal nocturnal dyspnea, orthopnea, coughing
What is meant by dyspnea on exertion?	Shortness of breath when active
What is meant by paroxysmal nocturnal dyspnea?	Sudden episodes of difficulty breathing
What is meant by orthopnea?	Shortness of breath when lying flat
Is heart rate fast or slow in pulmonary edema?	Fast, tachycardia
What will the nurse auscultate over the lungs when pulmonary edema occurs?	Crackles (rales)
When pulmonary edema is severe what does the sputum look like?	Bloody and frothy
What drug is used in pulmonary edema to reduce fluid in the lungs?	A diuretic Furosemide (Lasix)
What drug is used to increase ventilation in clients with pulmonary edema?	Aminophylline (bronchodilator)
Is O2 given in pulmonary edema?	Yes
Since pulmonary edema is caused by left ventricular failure what drug is given?	Digitalis
Why is morphine given to clients with pulmonary edema?	To decrease apprehension and decrease preload, this rests the heart.
If your client suddenly goes into pulmonary edema, what would you do first?	Elevate the HOB, then increase oxygen, then call HCP

PULMONARY EMBOLUS

Pulmonary embolus is an obstruction of the pulmonary _____ bed by a dislodged _____ or foreign substance.	Capillary, thrombus
Where do the emboli that cause pulmonary embolus usually come from?	The legs
Besides a thrombus what else can cause an embolus in the lung?	Air, fat, tumor cells
What treatment modality can lead to pulmonary embolus?	Bed rest
What class of drugs can lead to pulmonary embolus?	Oral contraceptives
What heart problem can lead to pulmonary embolus?	Atrial fibrillation (RIGHT atrial fibrillation causes pulmonary embolus; LEFT atrial fibrillation causes cerebral embolus.)
What genetic disorder can lead to pulmonary embolus?	Sickle cell anemia
What is the first sign of pulmonary embolus?	Dyspnea
The dyspnea of pulmonary embolus is accompanied by _____ _____.	Pleuritic pain
Does the heart rate increase or decrease in pulmonary embolus?	Increase
With severe pulmonary embolus the client will look as though they are _____.	In shock
What are the two major treatments of pulmonary embolus?	O2, anticoagulants
Name the anticoagulant given for immediate anticoagulation by IV or SQ route.	Heparin

A drug for long term anticoagulation in any disorder would be?	Warfarin
What two lab tests monitor warfarin therapy?	Prothrombin time (PT) and the INR.
When warfarin is therapeutic, the INR should be between _____ and _____.	2.0 and 3.9
What is Lovenox, Enoxaparin?	It is a low-dose Heparin used for anticoagulation in POST-OP THROMBOPHLEBITIS PREVENTIONNOT USED FOR PULMONARY EMBOLUS.
Heparin therapy is monitored by daily measurement of the _____.	PTT (partial thromboplastin time)
Effective heparin therapy raises the PTT to approximately _____ times normal.	2.5
Clients on heparin should use an electric razor or a safety razor?	Electric razor
What is the best way to prevent pulmonary embolus in post-operative patients?	Early ambulation
Is it appropriate to massage the legs of the client to prevent pulmonary embolus?	No, never
Heparin is used in the acute phase of pulmonary embolus. What drug is used for 6 months after pulmonary embolus?	Warfarin
Warfarin therapy is monitored by what daily test?	PT (prothrombin time)

PYELONEPHRITIS

What is pyelonephritis?	A bacterial infection of the kidneys
Which organism causes most pyelonephritis?	E. Coli
Name the symptoms that pyelonephritis and cystitis have in common?	Frequency, urgency, burning, cloudy, foul-smelling urine

What medical intervention is necessary in pyelonephritis?	IV antibiotics for one to two weeks, must get urine culture 2 weeks after antibiotic therapy is over.
How does pyelonephritis differ from Cystitis in meaning?	Cystitis means a bladder infection; pyelonephritis means an infection of kidney pelvis.
What causes or precedes pyelonephritis?	Cystitis always does
Will the client with pyelonephritis have daily weights?	Yes, as would any client with a kidney problem.
Name the five signs/symptoms that pyelonephritis has that cystitis does not have?	Fever, flank pain, chills, increased WBC, malaise
What is the BIG danger with pyelonephritis?	Permanent scarring and kidney damage.
How is pyelonephritis prevented?	By preventing or treating all cystitis (UTI's)
Will the client with pyelonephritis have hematuria?	It is common, but not always present.
The patient with pyelonephritis will have (hypertension/hypotension)?	Hypertension

RAYNAUD'S SYNDROME

Raynaud's is an arterial or venous disease?	Arterial disease characterized by spasms
What part of the body is most affected in Raynaud's?	The fingers
Raynaud's affects males or females mostly?	Women (young)
What three things precipitate a Raynaud's attack?	Exposure to cold, emotional stress, tobacco use
The digits in Raynaud's are hot or cold?	Cold
What will you find when you assess the legs of these patients?	Pale, sometimes blue

What three sensations will the client experience?	Weak/absent pulses, cool, pale, loss of hair, shiny thin skin
What will the fingers look like?	Pain, numbness, tingling
What should the client with Raynaud's avoid?	Cold weather. (They should wear gloves and stop smoking)

RENAL FAILURE

Give three stages of acute renal failure.	Oliguric, diuretic, recovery
Define renal failure.	Inability of the kidney to excrete wastes and maintain fluid and electrolyte balance.
What is the BIG danger in renal failure?	Hyperkalemia and its effect on the heart
What is anuria?	Less than 50 mL of urine out in 24 hours
What is oliguria?	Less than 500 mL of urine out in 24 hours
What are the dietary modifications for the recovery phase of acute renal failure?	Increased carbohydrates, increased protein
What are the dietary modifications for the diuretic phase of acute renal failure?	Increased carbohydrates, protein. Moderate potassium and sodium. (May need to increase fluids if diuresis results in dehydration.)
What are the dietary modifications for the oliguric phase of acute renal failure?	Increased carbohydrates, decreased protein, decreased sodium, decreased potassium, decreased water.
What causes the itching seen in renal failure?	Accumulation of wastes in the blood and the associated signs. This occurs in end stage renal failure.
What is the first phase in acute renal failure?	The oliguric phase.
In the oliguric phase, blood volume is _____, sodium is _____, and potassium is _____.	High, high, high
How long does the oliguric phase last?	7-10 days

In the diuretic phase: blood volume is _____, sodium is _____, and potassium is _____.	Low, low, low
How long does the diuretic phase usually last?	3-4 days, maximum time is 2-3 weeks
In the diuretic phase: urine output can = _____ to _____ liters / 24 hours.	4 - 5 liters per 24 hours
Which is more dangerous, oliguria or anuria? Why?	Oliguria, because since you are losing more fluids, you are actually hemo-concentrating the hyperkalemia more.

RESPIRATORY DISTRESS SYNDROME

Respiratory Distress Syndrome occurs in full-term infants. (T/F)	False, it occurs in premature infants.
Respiratory Distress Syndrome hardly ever occurs after week _____ of gestation.	37
Respiratory Distress Syndrome is also known as...	Hyaline Membrane Disease (HMD)
The cause of RDS is a lack of _____.	Surfactant
Surfactant _____ surface tension inside _____.	Decreases, alveoli
Surfactant prevents the _____ of the alveoli.	Collapse
Lack of surfactant causes the neonate to lose lung capacity with each _____.	Breath
Death from Respiratory Distress Syndrome most commonly occurs within _____ hours of birth.	96
Within minutes of birth, what 3 respiratory difficulties occur?	Retractions, nasal flaring, and grunting
What medication is given? By what route?	Survanta (Surfactant) via ET tube. Repeat doses are often required (Beractant)
What acid/base disorder is seen in Respiratory Distress Syndrome?	Respiratory acidosis (CO_2 is retained)

What will you auscultate over the lungs of the neonate with Respiratory Distress Syndrome?	Decreased lung sounds with crackles.
What lab test assesses the risk of Respiratory Distress Syndrome?	L/S ratio (Lecithin/Sphingomyelin ratio)
What L/S ratio indicates fetal lung maturity?	2/1
What other test is used to confirm fetal lung maturity?	Amniotic fluid is analyzed for presence of PG
Severe cases of Respiratory Distress Syndrome requires ventilation with _____.	PEEP (positive end expiratory pressure) and CPAP. (Continuous positive airway pressure), to keep the alveoli open while on the ventilator. High frequency jet ventilation is sometimes used.
What may be added to the IV to correct the acidosis?	Bicarbonate
High flow rates of O2 delivered in Respiratory Distress Syndrome can cause _____ _____.	Retrolental fibroplasia (an eye problem)
Retrolental fibroplasia can result in _____.	Blindness from retinal damage
High ventilatory pressures result in what chronic lung problems?	Broncho-pulmonary dysplasia

RHEUMATOID ARTHRITIS

At what time of year does rheumatoid arthritis flare up?	Spring
As with any inflammatory disease clients with rheumatoid arthritis have a low_____.	Grade fever
What factor is present in the blood when the client has rheumatoid arthritis?	The rheumatoid factor
As in most inflammatory diseases the client has an _____ erythrocyte sedimentation rate.	Increased
During an exacerbation (flare-up) of rheumatoid arthritis you should splint the joints in (extension/flexion).	Extension

As in most inflammatory disorders, the WBC count is _____. This is called _____.	Elevated; leukocytosis
What type of chair should be used for rheumatoid arthritis clients?	A chair with a high seat, armrests and one in which the knees are lower than the hips.
In rheumatoid arthritis the client should avoid positions of ___ and assume positions of ____.	Flexion, extension
When the client with rheumatoid arthritis is in remission you should apply (heat/cold) to the joint.	Heat
During an exacerbation of rheumatoid arthritis, you should apply (heat/ice).	Ice
Rheumatoid arthritis is more common in females than in males. (T/F)	True, unlike osteoarthritis, rheumatoid arthritis occurs three times more commonly in women.
People with rheumatoid arthritis (usually/ never) experience remission of symptoms.	Usually
Rheumatoid arthritis is a ____, _____ disease.	Chronic, inflammatory
Rheumatoid arthritis attacks the _____, _____, _____, _____, and _____ _____.	Joint, muscles, tendons, ligaments, blood vessels
Where are the nodules of rheumatoid arthritis found in contrast to the Heberden's nodes of osteoarthritis?	The nodes of rheumatoid arthritis are subcutaneous nodules usually on the elbows (ventral forearm); Heberden's nodes of osteoarthritis are on the fingers.
Which joints of the fingers are most affected by rheumatoid arthritis?	The proximal interphalangeal joint (PIP)
Clients with rheumatoid arthritis have a deformity of the wrist/hand called _____.	Swan-neck deformity
The mainstay of rheumatoid arthritis therapy is the drug _____.	Aspirin
Activity (increases/decreases) the pain of rheumatoid arthritis.	Decreases (This is opposite of osteoarthritis where activity increases the pain.)

Remissions of rheumatoid arthritis last for the rest of the patient's life. (T/F)	False, they usually have recurrence and when it re-occurs it usually comes back worse.

RIGHT-SIDED VS. LEFT-SIDED CHF

HINT: Remember left-sided causes mostly heart and lung problems; right-sided causes fluid back-up problems all over the body but not the lungs.

Dyspnea	Left
Cough	Left
Ascites	Right
Positive hepatojugular reflux	Right
Low cardiac output	Left
S3 and S4 gallops	Left
Crackles	Left
Pulses alternans	Left, strong pulse then a weak pulse alternatively.
Palpitations	Left
Fatigue	Left
Weight gain	Right
Diaphoresis	Left
Jugular vein pulsations	Right
Neck vein distention	Right
Hepatomegaly	Right
Edema	Right
Abdominal distention	Right

SCOLIOSIS

Scoliosis is a _____ curvature of the _____.	Lateral, spine
Scoliosis is <u>most</u> common in the _____ and _____ sections of the spinal column.	Thoracic and lumbar
Scoliosis in the thoracic spine is usually convex to the (left/right).	Right
Scoliosis in the lumbar spine is usually convex to the (left/right).	Left (*Hint: curve left in lumbar)
With which other two spine deformities is scoliosis associated?	Kyphosis (humpback) Lordosis (swayback)
What is Kyphosis?	Humpback in the thoracic area
What is Lordosis?	Swayback in the lumbar region (Lumbar, Lordosis
What is the difference between structural and functional scoliosis?	Structural--you are born with; Functional-- you get from bad posture.
What age group should be routinely screened for scoliosis?	Young teens
What are the three subjective complaints of clients with scoliosis?	Back pain, dyspnea, fatigue
What test/exam <u>confirms</u> the diagnosis of scoliosis?	X-rays of the spine
What type of brace is most commonly used for scoliosis?	Milwaukee
Name 4 exercises used to treat mild scoliosis.	Heel lifts; sit-ups; hyperextension of the spine; breathing exercises
What kind of treatment is done for severe scoliosis?	Surgical fusion with rod insertion
What type of cast is used post-operatively?	Risser cast
What kind of rod is used to "fix" curvature?	Harrington Rod

Scoliosis __most__ commonly affects _____ _____ (type of clients).	Teenage females
How many hours a day should the client wear a Milwaukee brace?	23
What solution should be used on the skin where the brace rubs?	Tincture of benzoin or alcohol, no lotions or ointments--you want to toughen the skin not soften it.
Clients with a Milwaukee brace should avoid vigorous exercise. (T/F)	TRUE
After corrective __surgery__, how is the client turned?	Log rolled (in a body cast)
How often should the neurovascular status of the extremities of a client in a Risser cast be measured? Fresh post-operatively?	Every 2 hours
What is a common complication of a client in a body cast (like the Risser cast)?	Cast syndrome
What is cast syndrome?	Nausea, vomiting and abdominal distention that can result in intestinal obstruction.
What group of people get cast syndrome?	Anyone in a body cast
What is the treatment for cast syndrome?	Removal of the cast, NG tube to decompress, NPO
How would you, the nurse, assess for developing cast syndrome?	Ask the client if they are experiencing any abdominal symptoms--keep track of bowel movements and passing flatus (if not having BMs or passing flatus, cast syndrome is suspected).
What causes cast syndrome, specifically in a Risser cast?	Hyperextension of the spine by a body cast: the hyperextension interrupts the nerve and blood supply to the gut.

SICKLE-CELL ANEMIA

The inheritance pattern of sickle-cell anemia is _____ _____.	Autosomal recessive
What does heterozygous mean?	It means you only have <u>one</u> defective gene from only <u>one</u> parent.
People who are (hetero/homo) zygous have sickle cell **trait**.	Heterozygous
What does homozygous mean?	It means you have the defective gene from both parents.
People who are (hetero/homozygous?) have sickle cell **disease**.	Homozygous
People with sickle cell <u>trait</u> only carry the disease, they <u>do not</u> have symptoms. (T/F)	True, usually it has occurred that in times of <u>severe</u> stress, the <u>trait</u> does cause some symptoms but not usually.
What are the #1 and #2 causes of sickle cell crisis?	Hypoxia, dehydration
The most common type of crisis that occurs is a _____-_____ crisis.	Vaso-occlusive
In vaso-occlusive crisis the vessels become occluded with _____ _____.	Abnormal RBCs
The abnormal hemoglobin produced by people with sickle cell anemia is called Hgb _____.	Hgb S-it "sickles"
What shape does Hgb S make the RBCs?	Crescent-shaped
Why do the crescent-shaped RBCs cause occlusion of the vessels?	They clump together and create a sludge.
What are the top 3 priorities in care of the client with sickle-cell crisis?	Oxygenation, hydration, and <u>pain control</u>
What activity order will the client with sickle cell crisis have?	Bed rest

Of Tylenol, Morphine, Demerol, Aspirin, which is never given to sickle-cell patients?	Aspirin can cause acidosis which makes the crisis and sickling worse.
At what age is death most likely in sickle cell anemia?	Young adulthood
Sickle-cell anemia symptoms do not appear before the age of _____ months due to the presence of _____ _____.	6; fetal hemoglobin
Sickle cell anemia is most commonly seen in (African Americans/Anglo Americans).	African Americans
Should a child in sickle-cell crisis wear tight clothes?	No, it can occlude vessels even more.

SPINAL CORD INJURY

Spinal cord injuries are more common in males. (T/F)	TRUE
In what age range is spinal cord injury most common?	15 to 25
The #1 goal in emergency treatment of spinal cord injury is...	Immobilization of the spine
When halo traction is being used to immobilize the spinal cord, the client is allowed to _____.	Ambulate
When the patient with spinal cord injury is in tongs or on a stryker frame or on a circoelectric bed they are on...	Absolute bed rest
The two most common surgeries used to treat spinal cord injury are _____ and _____ _____.	Laminectomy and spinal fusion
What is spinal shock?	It is a common occurrence in spinal cord injury in which the spinal cord swells above and below the level of injury.

When does spinal shock occur?	Immediately or within 2 hours of injury
How long does spinal shock last?	5 days to 3 months
When the spinal cord injury is at level of _____ to _____ the patient will be quadriplegic.	C1 to C8
When spinal cord injury is between _____ and _____, there is permanent respiratory paralysis.	C1 and C4
Can the patient with spinal cord injury at C7 level have respiratory arrest?	Yes, because even though his injury was below C4, spinal shock can lead to loss of function above the level, however he will not be permanently ventilator dependent--he will breathe on own once spinal shock goes away.
Spinal cord injury in the thoracic/lumbar regions result in _____plegia.	Paraplegia
If airway obstruction occurs at the accident site and you suspect spinal cord injury, what maneuver is used to open the airway?	Modified jaw thrust
In spinal cord injury never _____ the neck.	Move, hyperextend
How should you change the position of the spinal cord injury patient after he has an order to be up? Why?	Slowly, because of severe orthostatic hypotension (they use a tilt table).
For the patient with a neurogenic bladder, you should straight catheterize every _____ hours.	Every 6 hours
The patient with spinal cord injury will have (flaccid/spastic) muscles.	Spastic
Name 3 drugs used to treat spasms?	Diazepam (Valium), Baclofen, Dantrium

What is autonomic dysreflexia or hyperreflexia?	A common complication of quadriplegics in response to a full bladder or bowel.
What are the vital sign changes seen in autonomic dysreflexia?	Sweating, headache, nausea and vomiting, gooseflesh, and severe HYPERtension.
What do you do first for the client experiencing autonomic dysreflexia?	Raise HOB
What do you do second in the patient experiencing autonomic dysreflexia?	Check the bladder, check the bowel
Do you need to call the doctor for autonomic dysreflexia?	No, only call the doctor if draining the bladder and removing impaction does not work.
What is the #1 treatment for autonomic dysreflexia?	Drain the bladder, empty the bowel

SYPHILIS

Syphilis is sexually transmitted. (T/F)	TRUE
Syphilis first infects the _____ _____.	Mucous membranes
What are the stages of syphilis?	Primary, secondary, latent, late
Syphilis is a fatal disease if untreated. (T/F)	TRUE
What organism causes syphilis?	Treponema palladium
What is the lesion like in primary syphilis?	The chancre (pronounced shanker)
The chancres of syphilis are (painful/painless).	Painless
Chancres disappear without treatment. (T/F)	TRUE
Late syphilis attacks which 3 body organs?	Liver, heart, brain

What test confirms the presence of syphilis?	Dark-field illumination of the treponema palladium
What is the treatment of choice for syphilis?	Penicillin
Why is penicillin administered with Procaine? With Probenecid?	Procaine makes the shot less painful; Probenecid blocks the excretion of penicillin
What is the most common sign of neurosyphilis?	Ataxia (gait problems)

THORACENTESIS

In what group of clients is thoracentesis contraindicated?	Uncooperative, bleeding disorders
What instruction is most important to give the client undergoing thoracentesis?	Don't move or cough
What is thoracentesis?	The pleural space is entered by puncture and fluid is drained by gravity into drainage devices--allows the lungs to re-expand.
If a client has a cough, what should be done before thoracentesis?	Give him a cough suppressant
Does thoracentesis require a signed informed consent?	Yes, it invades a body cavity.
Describe the position the client should assume during a thoracentesis?	Upright with arms and shoulders elevated, slightly leaning forward.

THYROID FACTS

What is exophthalmos?	Bulging outward of eyes
To care for the patient with exophthalmos the patient should wear _____ _____ and use _____ _____.	Dark sunglasses, artificial tears

Radioactive iodine is given to hyperthyroid patients because it _____ _____ plus decreases production of _____ _____.	Destroys tissue, thyroid hormone
The #1 problem with using Propylthiouracil is _____.	Agranulocytosis
What do you teach to all patients on drugs which have agranulocytosis as a side effect?	Report any sore throat immediately.
Lugols solution decreases the _____ of the thyroid gland.	Vascularity
Lugols solution should be given _____ a _____ to prevent staining of the _____.	Through a straw; teeth
SSKI should be given with _____ _____ to decrease the _____ _____.	Fruit juices; bitter taste (SSKI--super saturated solution of potassium iodide)
Patients with either hypo or hyper thyroid can go into thyroid storm. (T/F?)	TRUE
Give another name for thyroid storm.	Thyrotoxicosis, thyroid crisis
In thyrotoxicosis, the temperature ____; the heart rate ____ and the patient becomes ____.	Increases (106°); increases; delirious/comatose
What is the first thing a nurse does when thyroid storm occurs?	Give oxygen
What is the second thing a nurse does when thyroid crisis occurs?	Call HCP, can pack in ice or use hypothermia blanket.
What are the side effects of thyroid replacement drugs?	Tachycardia, palpitations, and other signs seen in hyperthyroidism.
Why is Lugols solution given pre-operatively thyroidectomy?	To decrease the vascularity of the gland and minimize blood loss.
After thyroidectomy you check for wound hemorrhage by...	Slipping your hand under the neck and shoulders

The #1 complication of thyroidectomy in the first 8 to 12 hours is _____.	Hemorrhage--or maybe airway
When moving the fresh post-operative thyroidectomy patient, you must take care to never _____ _____ _____.	Move the neck
Post-operatively thyroidectomy patients will have sandbags on either side of the _____.	Neck
Why do you assess the post-operative thyroidectomy patient's voice for hoarseness periodically?	Because during surgery the surgeon may have nicked the recurrent laryngeal nerve. (This nerve is tested on state boards!)
Will the post-operative thyroidectomy patient be allowed to talk?	He is on voice rest unless you are assessing his voice.
In what position should the post-operative thyroidectomy patient be?	Semi-fowlers with neck supported in midline
What three pieces of emergency equipment must be in the room after thyroid storm?	Suction, tracheotomy set, oxygen
What calcium imbalance is common in the post-op throidectomy patient?	Hypocalcemia--due to accidental removal of the parathyroids
When is hypocalcemia most likely to occur after thyroidectomy? Why?	The second and third postoperative day-because it takes a while for the level to drop.
Hypocalcemia will cause (tetany/severe muscle weakness).	Tetany
What drug is used to treat decreased calcium?	Calcium gluconate
What is Chvostek's sign?	A sign of hypocalcemia, it is when you tap the cheek, the patient puffs out the cheeks. (CHvostek and CHeeks)
What is Trousseau's sign?	It is a sign of hypocalcemia--it is when you get a carpopedal spasm of the hand when you apply a blood pressure cuff to the lower arm.
What is the earliest sign of hypocalcemia?	Tremors/tingling

Should you palpate the thyroid of the hyperthyroid patient after ectomy?	No, it could send them into thyroid storm
Can dental work send a hyperthyroid client into a thyroid storm?	Yes, any stress can

TRACHEO-ESOPHAGEAL MALFORMATION

What is meant by tracheo-esophageal malformation?	These are a group of congenital birth defects in which the esophagus and trachea are malformed.
How many types of tracheo-esophageal malformations are there?	Four
What are the three most common tracheoesophageal malformations?	1)Esophageal atresia-EA, 2) Tracheoesophageal fistula-TEF, 3)Tracheo-esophageal fistula with esophageal atresia-TEF w/EA
What is the defect called esophageal fistula?	An opening between the esophagus and trachea, but the esophagus is connected to the stomach and trachea is connected to the lungs.
What is the defect called tracheo-esophageal atresia with fistula?	The esophagus ends in a blind pouch and there is no connection to the stomach and there is a fistula between the esophagus and trachea.
Of: tracheo-esophageal fistula, esophageal atresia, and tracheo-esophageal atresia with fistula, which one is most common?	Tracheo-esophageal fistula with esophageal atresia
Name - a blind end esophagus: the trachea is connected to the lungs.	Simple esophageal atresia
Name - the trachea is connected to the lungs, the esophagus is connected to the stomach, but there is a hole connecting the trachea and the esophagus.	Tracheo-esophageal fistula
Name - a blind end esophagus, the trachea is connected to the lungs, and the trachea and esophagus are joined.	Tracheo-esophageal fistula with esophageal atresia

If an infant has tracheo-esophageal fistula with esophageal atresia what three signs will show up at the first feeding?	Three C's-coughing, choking, cyanosis
If an infant chokes, coughs, or gets cyanotic during the first feeding what should the nurse do to ASSESS for tracheo-esophageal fistula with esophageal atresia?	Attempt to gently pass a catheter into the esophagus if you meet resistance STOP, there most probably is esophageal atresia.
How is the diagnosis of tracheo-esophageal fistula with esophageal atresia confirmed?	X-ray with barium
Prior to surgery for repair of tracheoesophageal fistula with esophageal atresia, how is the infant fed?	They are NPO but fed by G-tube (gastrostomy)
Does a tracheo-esophageal fistula with esophageal atresia have to be repaired immediately?	No, can be maintained with G-tube feedings and suctioning until they are old enough and stable enough to tolerate surgery.
The #1 problem for infants with unrepaired tracheo-esophageal fistula with esophageal atresia is...	Aspiration, secondary problem is malnutrition
How do you meet the oral sucking needs that an infant with un-repaired tracheoesophageal fistula with esophageal atresia?	Use pacifiers, even though they don't take anything orally, they should still be encouraged to suck.
How should an infant with tracheoesophageal fistula with esophageal atresia be positioned?	HOB up 30°
Should you suction the blind esophageal pouch of esophageal atresia?	Yes, PRN, otherwise they may aspirate mucus.

TRACHEOSTOMY CARE

What is the most common cleansing solution used during tracheostomy care?	Hydrogen peroxide
Cut the old trach ties (before/after) you have secured the new ties in place.	After

Is it acceptable to scrub the inside of the tracheostomy cannula with a brush during tracheostomy care?	Yes, it is desirable.
What are the two major reasons for performing tracheostomy care?	To keep the airway patent, to keep the stoma site clean (decrease infection)
Tie the ends of the trach ties in a (bow knot/double knot).	Only a double knot
Trach care is performed by (clean/sterile) technique.	Sterile
What must you do before performing trach care (besides wash hands)?	Suction the airway
A properly snug set of trach ties allows _____ finger(s) to be placed between the neck and ties.	One
Both hands must be kept sterile throughout the entire trach care procedure. (T/F)	False, only the dominant hand remains sterile.
When trach suctioning and care is performed by the client at home, sterile technique must be followed. (T/F)	False, clean technique is adequate.

TRIGEMINAL NEURALGIA

What is another name for trigeminal neuralgia?	Tic douloureux
Which cranial nerve is affected in trigeminal neuralgia?	Cranial nerve 5
What is the #1 symptom of trigeminal neuralgia?	Episodic, severe one-sided facial pain
What drug treats trigeminal neuralgia?	Carbamazepine (Tegretol)
What triggers attacks of trigeminal neuralgia?	Breezes, cold or hot foods/fluids, tooth brushing, chewing, touching the face, talking
Is surgery done for trigeminal neuralgia?	Yes, nerve avulsion (destroying the nerve)

What environmental modifications are necessary in care of the patient with trigeminal neuralgia?	Prevent drafts or temperature extremes
After surgery for trigeminal neuralgia, the patient's affected eye will be _____ and the patient should chew food on the _____ side.	Protected; unaffected

TUBERCULOSIS

What organism causes pulmonary TB?	Mycobacterium tuberculosis
The mode of transmission of the mycobacterium tuberculosis organism is by _____ _____.	Droplet nuclei
What living conditions predispose you to TB?	Crowded, poorly ventilated
The incubation period of tuberculosis is....	4 to 8 weeks
What is the typical lung lesion of TB called?	A tubercle
In TB, the appetite is _____; the client _____ weight and the temperature _____ in the _____.	Decreased, loses, elevates, afternoon
What is a Mantoux test?	An intradermal skin test to screen for TB-called PPD
When should a Mantoux test be read?	48 to 72 hours after test injection
What qualifies as a positive Mantoux?	More than 10 mm induration (hardness), remember redness has nothing to do with the test being positive.
Name three drugs given to treat TB.	Isoniazid, Rifampin, Ethambutol
How often and when during the day should Isoniazid, Rifampin, and Ethambutol be given?	Every day, all together.
What is the #1 side effect of Isoniazid?	Peripheral neuritis--take vitamin B6 to prevent

After how many weeks of drug therapy is the client considered NO LONGER contagious?	2 to 4 weeks
What isolation techniques are required for TB?	Masks
Which test is most diagnostic for TB?	Sputum for acid-fast bacilli
What does the sputum look like in TB?	Purulent (pus) or hemoptysis (blood)
When should you obtain a sputum specimen for acid fast bacilli TB?	Early AM

ULCERATIVE COLITIS VS. CROHN'S DISEASE

Clear liquid diet	Ulcerative colitis
Bed rest	Ulcerative colitis
Women mostly	Ulcerative colitis
One-layer ulcerations with edema of bowel	Ulcerative colitis
Steroids	Either
I & O	Either
Rectum and sigmoid colon	Ulcerative colitis
Bloody diarrhea	Ulcerative colitis
Young adults	Ulcerative colitis

Surgery with ileostomy	Either
Ileostomy	Either
Jewish clients	Either
Lesion through all layers of the bowel	Crohn's
Terminal-distal-small intestine	Crohn's
Regional enteritis	Crohn's
Adults, up to 40	Crohn's
Lesions form patches	Crohn's
Sulfa drugs	Crohn's
Granulomas	Crohn's-hint: "gran"ny Crohn
"String sign" on barium enema	Crohn's
Diarrhea	Crohn's
Pain and cramping	Crohn's
Steroids (Prednisone)	Either

Made in the USA
Columbia, SC
29 July 2024